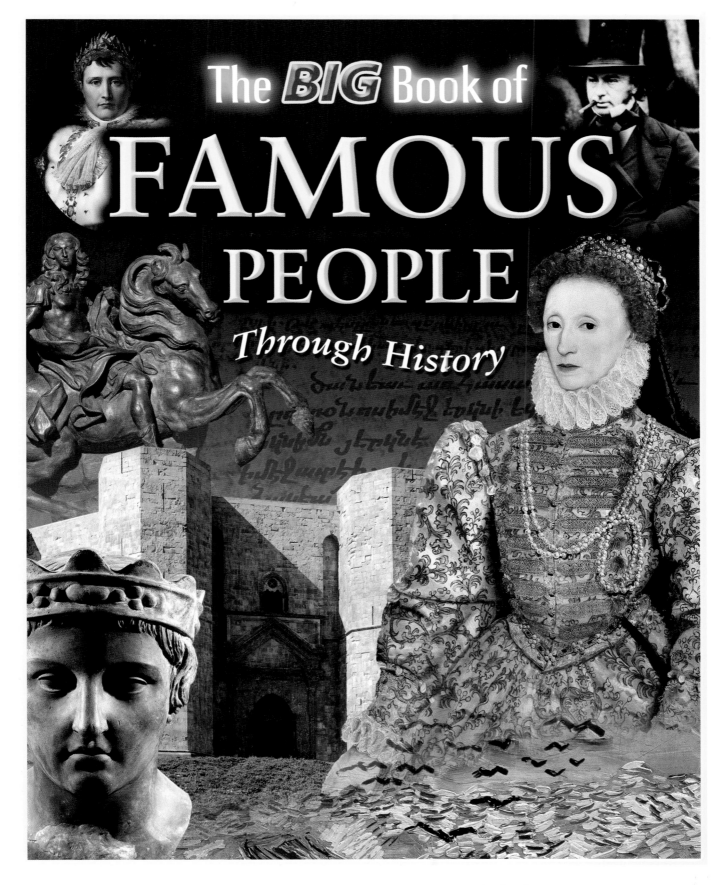

The BIG Book of
FAMOUS
PEOPLE
Through History

English edition translated from the Italian and edited
by Maureen Spurgeon

Brown Watson
ENGLAND

Original Italian text and editorial content: Laura Tassi
Production Editor: Stefano Sibella
Graphics and covers: Viviana Cerrato
Pagination: Marco and Matteo Volpati (Fox Studio)
Editor, technical content: Gianluigi Ronchetti
Picture research: Laura Tassi, Federica Magrin

Illustrations supplied by picture agencies:
Photographs and drawings, DeAgostini Picture Library:
photograph, p.96 – Marco Volpati
Photographs, pp. 44, 55,64,70,74,137,171,175,176 – Federica Magrin

ISBN: 0-7097-1712-1

Il Grande Libro delle Domande & Risposte
© 2004 De Agostini Editore S.p.A., Novara
© 2006 Brown Watson, English edition

The **BIG** Book of

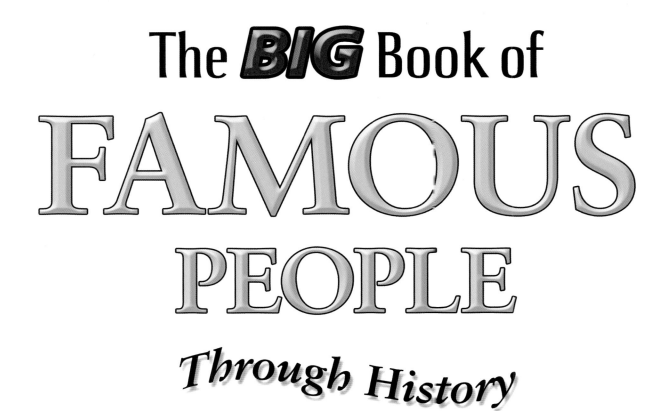

FAMOUS

PEOPLE

Through History

Contents

MATHEMATICIANS
PHYSICISTS
and
INVENTORS

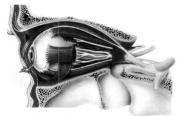

> *The mathematical genius who 'raised the Earth with a lever'*

ARCHIMEDES
(Syracuse circa 287 BC – 212 BC)

The people of Syracuse strolled along, stopping at street corners to chat or to go into shops to buy things. Suddenly, the peace was shattered when a man appeared out of nowhere. Bathed in sweat, his face red and quite breathless, he managed to cry 'Eureka!' (in the Greek language 'I've found it!') before disappearing again. Archimedes, that extrovert genius, who, according to the stories of Plutarch, went without food whilst he continued his mathematical studies, had discovered how the king had been cheated. Whilst in his bath, it suddenly occurred to Archimedes how a goldsmith had cheated the king by supplying a new crown which was not pure gold. Without stopping even to put on his clothes, he ran outside to tell everyone about it.

The life of Archimedes is a mixture of reality and legend. Even his birth is shrouded in mystery. The date 287 BC is simply a subtraction from the date of his death in 212 BC; we know that when he was seventy-five years old, he was killed by a Roman soldier at the end of the siege of Syracuse. In one of his works, *Arenarius ('the sand-reckoner')*, which sets out a complicated method for the calculation of heavenly bodies, Archimedes refers to being the son of Phidias, an astronomer. In his youth, he had a habit of travelling in the course of his studies. He finally settled in Egypt at Alexandria, where the king Ptolemy had gathered many outstanding exponents in the fields of science and the arts. There, Archimedes found an environment which welcomed his mathematical researches – so much so, that when he returned home, he remained in constant communication by letter with the leading scholars at Alexandria.

View of Alexandria, Egypt

Returning to Syracuse, Archimedes distinguished himself with his ingenuity by which he succeeded in solving, with skill and amazing practical sense, numerous problems, the first being the launching of the ship *Syracusia*. The life of Archimedes carried on peacefully with theories in the field of geometry (*On the Sphere and the Cylinder; On spirals; On the Centre of Gravity of Planes*) and plans of fantastic inventions, such as the **orrery**, (a mechanical model of the solar system) and the **hydraulic screw**, until the time when Gelon became king on the death of Hieron, who had reigned for ten years as an ally of Rome. In 213 AD, Roman troops led by Marcus Claudius Marcellus took control of Syracuse. Archimedes, who had served the city in times of peace, applied his genius to designing many war machines to defend the city. The following year, the Romans broke down the Syracuse defence and invaded the city. Archimedes, powerless, could not stop the brutality and continued with his calculations and studies, until the moment of the blow which killed him. A soldier caused the death of Archimedes, although the commander of the Roman troops had ordered his life to be spared.

Archimedes and da Vinci

Leonardo da Vinci carefully studied the work of Archimedes and built many prototypes based on his inventions – such as the famous 'hydraulic screw' (photograph above). The Italian inventor also unearthed a story about a journey made by Archimedes in Spain. Here, da Vinci discovered that Archimedes had built some defence mechanisms to help the people of Cilodastri, but no other information had been recorded.

The siege of Syracuse, as illustrated by Pogliaghi

A ship raised by a lever

The *Syracusia* was an important ship (it weighed more than 4,200 tonnes) and was built by Heiron II, king of Syracuse, to give to the king of Egypt as a sign of friendship. But the ship was so huge that it seemed impossible to launch it into the water. Archimedes invented a system of pulley and lever (shown in the illustration, right) which, worked by a simple touch of the hand, could lift the ship. This is the origin of the proverbial phrase 'give me a place to stand, and I will move the world' – which refers to the lever.

Altar of Hieron at Syracuse

The 'many deaths' of Archimedes

There are many different versions of the killing of Archimedes. According to some, the mathematician was killed because, engrossed in his studies, he refused to surrender to Marcello; others claim that he was assassinated by a handful of soldiers convinced that he had hidden gold in his workshops; it is also said that, ignoring the danger which threatened, Archimedes was drawing geometric figures in the dust when he was stabbed to death.

The dictator Hieron

Some historians, such as **Plutarch**, say that Archimedes was bound by a deep friendship and, perhaps, by parental bonds to the king of Syracuse, **Hieron II**. The illegitimate son of a noble, Hieron was crowned king of Syracuse in 270 BC, and, thanks to a knowledge of politics and an alliance with Rome, he was able to promise independence and the prospect of free trade to the people. Due to the respect which Archimedes had for this 'enlightened' dictator, he frequently set aside his own work to concentrate on the requests of Heiron – such as the invention of the **charistion**, a system of levers which were used for the launch of the ship *Syracusia*, and the hydraulic screw (or Archimedes' screw) a device for the raising of water.

Altar of Hieron at Syracuse

The Rule of Archimedes explains how great ships can remain afloat

Genius in the bath

Many scientists have had important inspirations in unusual places. For Archimedes, that place was the bath-tub! Whilst he was soaking himself in the water, not only did he discover how a dishonest goldsmith had cheated King Hieron, but also the reason why objects floated on water. This idea, known afterwards as the 'Archimedes' Principle' (or Rule of Archimedes) established that when an object is immersed in water, this object gets a thrust towards the surface which is equal to the weight of the quantity of liquid which is displaced – as if the object were on one dish of a balance scale and the volume of liquid displaced had been put into the other dish of the same balance scale.

Archimedes in his bath-tub

Science in war

The defence mechanisms invented by Archimedes soon became a nightmare for the Roman soldiers – catapults which could hit ships at a considerable distance; cranes able to aim at the enemy with incredible precision, enormous beams with great iron hooks to seize the prow of a ship and make it sink …

Over the centuries, Archimedes has been credited with many feats – such as setting fire to Roman ships by **burning mirrors** – systems of reflective surfaces large enough to burn objects at a distance. In 1973 Dr. Ioannis Sakkas tested the idea with the help of nearly 60 Greek sailors, each holding a large oblong mirror angled to catch the Sun's rays and point them at a wooden rowboat 160 feet away. The boat instantly caught fire.

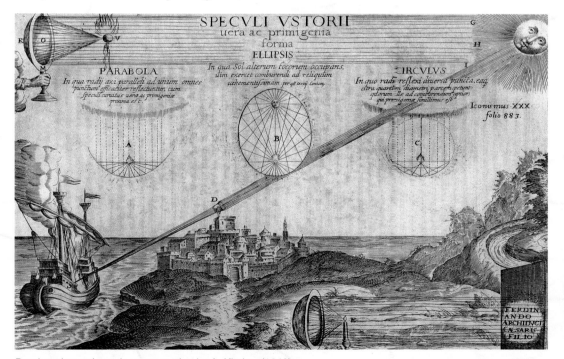

Burning glass mirrors in an engraving by A. Kircher (1646)

The astronomer who moved the Earth from the centre of the Universe

NICOLAUS COPERNICUS

(Torun, Poland 1473 – Frauenburg, Poland 1543)

A warm, happy atmosphere spread throughout Frauenburg, a city in Warmja (now Poland) on the Baltic Sea. It was 24 May 1543 and the perfumes of spring-time wafted along the streets and through the windows of the city convent. Here, a clergyman unable to move, lay in his bed, watched over by his fellow monks. His body was already worn away, but his mind had not yet yielded to death. Suddenly the door burst open and in came a man holding up a book. The sick man managed to take the book in his hands, tracing the cover with the point of his finger. Then, smiling, he finally left the Earth with the thought that it had been removed from the centre of the Universe.

The *De revolutionibus orbium coelestium* was a work which was destined to revolutionize completely the future studies of astronomy. It came to be printed after many long years of hard work, and in 1543 a copy was delivered to Nicholas Copernicus, the author, just a little while before his death. It was the crowning moment of a long research, which the Polish scientist had been doing for more than thirty years, since 1510. In his work *Commentariolus* (*Little Commentary*, published only in the 18th century) Copernicus had already set out in 1514 his own and entirely new vision of the cosmos – a system with the Sun at the centre, and not the Earth, as was believed at the time. However, despite this important assertion, Copernicus did not dedicate himself totally to investigating the mysteries of the Universe. From his youth, innumerable interests and other passions led him to undertake a series of personal journeys to the main cities of northern Italy.

Copernicus Square at Warsaw, Poland

The first stop was Bologna, where he arrived with his brother Andreas in 1496. Although he was enrolled at the University as a student of law, Copernicus attended the lessons given by the astronomer **Domenico Maria de Novara** more regularly. After three years, he left the city without having obtained the title of Doctor of Law (he achieved this much later, in 1503, at Ferrara).

The same thing happened at Padua, where he studied medicine without finishing his studies. Both disciplines, **law** and **medicine** were most valuable to him later on, when he became a priest. As assistant to the Bishop of Ermland, he was employed in administrative and political tasks, as well as the duties of a doctor. His main function was that of '**quartermaster**' a public official who supervised the supply of food and the upkeep of furnaces and windmills. The respect shown towards him by his superiors was such that he was often occupied in areas far removed from astronomy, law and medicine. In fact, Copernicus had a brilliant career, moving back and forth from his astronomical discoveries to travel and studies in various fields of knowledge.

Astrolabe, an instrument used to establish the correct position of the stars in the sky

The city of Torun

Copernicus and astronomy

Copernicus first became interested in astronomy on the clear night of 9 March 1497. This was the date of a rare eclipse – the passage of Aldebaran, a star in the constellation of Taurus, moving in front of the moon. Observing this exceptional astronomical event profoundly struck his imagination – and although Copernicus had enrolled as a student of law at Bologna University (photograph, left; the **theatre of anatomy**) he spent more time observing the night sky than studying law.

A blot on his reputation

Although he was a famous astronomer and scholar, there was no lack of scandal and controversy in the life of Nicholas Copernicus. First, many people resented the fact that he achieved his powerful position at Warmja mainly because his uncle was the Bishop. Also, it came to light only when Copernicus was over sixty years old that, although he had held the title of Canon for many years, he had never taken the religious vows of a priest or been ordained. But, in the end, none of this detracted from his theory which led to the **Copernican revolution**, heralding a completely new concept of the universe.

The astronomer, from the painting by Jan Vermeer

A world which is transformed...

In the second century AD, the Greek mathematician and geographer **Claudius Ptolemy** had set out in his work *Syntaxis Mathematica* (known by the Arabic title *Almagest*) his own astronomical theory. According to this, the Earth was quite still and positioned at the centre of the Universe, with the Sun and the other planets moving around it. But some aspects of his theory did not agree when it was seen how some stars moved. The first to realize

this was Ptolemy himself, who had based his astronomical system on a series of estimates and concepts to make his calculations add up. Then in the 1400s, **Nicholas Copernicus,** disillusioned by so much inaccuracy and obvious guesswork in Ptolemy's theory, finally reached the right conclusion – that the Sun was the centre of the cosmos and the Earth, whilst spinning on its own axis, moved around the Sun in a regular orbit. This vision of the Universe

The geographer Ptolemy holding the globe of the Earth

also had some faults – the main one being that he believed that the orbit of planets was circular (instead of elliptic, meaning oval); but this did not weaken the tremendous effect of Copernicus' proven theory, soon defined as the **Copernican revolution**.

Structure of the Universe according to Copernicus

...and a science which moves on

After Copernicus, the scientific world did not remain still. Whilst philosophers and clerics raised questions about how people would react and how their views about their lives on Earth might change, scientists of the day investigated the claims of Copernicus which he had published in *De revolutionibus*. Some scholars, although accepting the heliocentric theory (that the Sun was the centre of the Universe) introduced their own substantial modifications to the theories of Copernicus. The German mathematician **Johannes Kepler** (1571–1630) carefully analyzed the relationship between the distance of each planet and the time it took to complete its orbit. Kepler also established that each orbit was elliptical, and not circular, as Copernicus had claimed. Others, including Kepler's employer, Danish-born **Tycho Brahe** (1546–1601) maintained that Ptolemy's astronomical model was still best, but with modifications; for instance – that the planets moved around the Sun and not Earth, but the Sun moved around the Earth which remained quite still at the centre of the Universe.

Neptune and Pluto. Pluto was discovered only in 1930. Even science itself continues to move on!

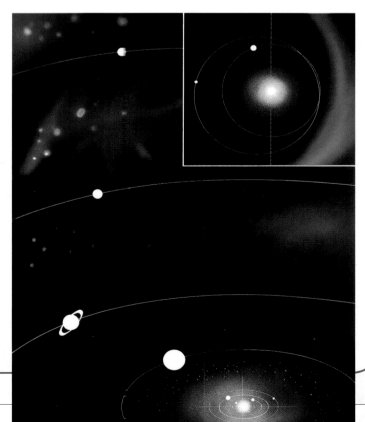

The courageous scientist who first observed the night sky through a telescope

GALILEO GALILEI

(Pisa 1564 – Acetri, Florence 1642)

The room was silent and quite dark, except for a beam of dusty light. At the centre, stood an old man (sixty-nine years old) his eyes staring into space as he waited to hear the verdict of the ten cardinals forming the Inquisition – putting him on trial for going against the word of the Bible. By the time they returned, the fate of the scientist Galileo Galilei had been decided. Very soon, he would be forced to reject his own scientific theories, to save himself from torture and death. On 22 June 1633, he made a declaration in which he 'renounced, cursed and detested' his own beliefs in the theories of Nicholas Copernicus. The Church did not allow Galileo to appeal and he was incarcerated in his house at Acetri, under the strict control of the religious authorities. It was here that he explained his own theories many years later, in 1642, by which time he was blind and alone.

View of the dockyard at Venice today

The phases of the Moon, from Galileo's *Sidereus Nuncius*

Galileo Galilei was born in Pisa in 1564, where his family had moved from Florence. As well as being a wool merchant, his father **Vincenzo Galilei** was an educated scholar and lute-player. Galileo inherited his father's passion for music and education, but was soon directing his own interests towards the sciences, especially mathematics. In 1591, on the death of his father, the family finances became disastrous. As the eldest son,

Galileo had to look after his mother, his brother and his sisters. Financial problems were to worry him all his life and were the reason for some choices he had to make – for example, the decision to leave Venice, which later proved unwise. In 1610, Galileo gave up the Chair of Mathematics at the University of Padua to take on the role of scientist at the court of the Grand Duke of Tuscany. Here there was a short time of peace for Galileo, during which he concentrated on his own investigations into the phases of the planet Venus, the composition of the lunar soil and the movement of the stars. Then, in Florence, word began to spread about his support for the theories of Copernicus, which, church leaders said, contradicted what was written in the Bible. Hot-tempered and obstinate by nature, Galileo's protests only inflamed the debate. There were angry exchanges of words, followed by accusations, then came the inquisition of the cardinals and their judgement which wrecked the final years of his life. But the isolation and the disillusion did not stop Galileo finishing his experiments on motion, and in 1638, the manuscript of his book *Discorsi e dimostrazioni matematiche intorno a due nuove scienze (Discourse and mathematical demonstrations on two new sciences)* was smuggled to Leiden in Holland to be published. The theories on motion written in this book were the basis for the studies of **Isaac Newton**, the English physicist, who was born in the same year as Galileo died.

Galileo imprisoned; painting by Benevello della Chiesa

Science in a common language

Galileo made an important step in the spread of scientific knowledge. By the 14th century, the languages of different countries were being widely used in writing and literature. Yet, even in the 17th century, scientists communicated with each other solely in Latin. But by this time, Latin had lost a lot of its impact and had become inadequate in describing physical phenomenon which had been observed, thanks to new instruments. Latin was also an 'elite' language, studied and learned mainly by those attending University and unknown to most other people. Galileo was aware of all the limitations of Latin and so he used two languages in his writings – **Latin** for those parts of the text aimed at other students and scientists, as in the title *Sidereus Nuncius* (photograph, right) and the **common language** for those writings directed towards a wider public – for example in the *Dialogo sopra I due massimi sistemi del mondo* (*Dialogue on the two chief world systems – Ptolemaic and Copernican*).

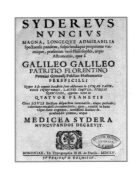

The use of the common language also meant that Galileo (and later, other scientists) could write in a clearer, more simple way so that he was able to explain complex mathematical formulations more easily, sometimes in the form of a dialogue between people from different backgrounds and with different views on the subject in question. All this meant that people who could read were able to increase their scientific knowledge and awareness, whatever their background and whether they were rich or poor.

Galileo and his daughters

In 1613, Galileo made his daughters **Virginia** and **Livia** enter the Convent of St Matthew in Acetri, so that he would not have to provide a marriage dowry for them. This act, perhaps motivated also by the illegitimate birth (born outside marriage) of the two girls, contrasted sharply with the care he showed the rest of his family, especially his adored brother Michelo.

Livia never forgave her father for making her take religious vows, but Virginia accepted her father's decision and was the only person to stay close to Galileo in the dramatic moments which followed the Inquisition. Her premature death in 1634 was a shattering blow to Galileo. From that moment he was completely alone, as well as progressively losing his sight.

Galileo experiments with gravity

With the Hubble Space Telescope, the observation of the sky is possible in outer space.

Below, the pendulum clock designed by Galileo

The telescope

In 1608 in Holland, Hans Lippershey had made an instrument with two lenses which enabled a person to see objects as if they were much closer. Galileo, always looking for instruments to sell to the Venetian government and interested in anything new in the field of technology, heard about it, worked out the principle himself and made his own telescope. Although the discovery was not his, he does have the credit of being the first to use the telescope to study the night sky. This had amazing consequences – the discovery of the satellites of Jupiter, the study of the surface of the Moon, the observation of Sun spots ... by using the telescope, Galileo became a pioneer in astronomy.

Thanks to the telescope (below, right) Galileo carried out important astronomical observations, such as the identification of Sun spots (left)

The instruments of Galileo

Whilst Professor of Mathematics at the University of Padua, Galileo spent much of his spare time at the docks at Venice, also in the studios of the Venetian glass-workers, and in workshops of mechanics where he made machines and other devices for war. All these activities at a young age enabled Galileo to understand the value of experiments and scientific demonstration, as well as the observation of natural phenomena and how these could be reproduced in a laboratory. Galileo also invented many technical instruments, such as the **thermometer** (an instrument for measuring heat) the **geometric compass, water pumps, microscopes** ... some to enable the impoverished Galileo to earn money, others to make his own scientific investigations easier.

The mathematician who discovered the force of gravity.

ISAAC NEWTON
(Woolsthorpe 1642 – London 1726)

A boy walked through the countryside of Woolsthorpe in England, one step following another, taking no notice of the thatched roof cottages, the bleating of the sheep and the peasants working hard in the fields. Immersed in his own thoughts, he sat down in the shade of an apple tree, looking up at the fruit hanging from the branches. 'Why do the apples hang downwards? Why does the Moon stay close to the Earth? What happens in the heavens that is different to what happens on our planet?' These were some of the questions which the young Isaac Newton asked himself one day in 1666, sitting under a tree in the grounds of the house where he was born.

Nobody can be sure if the story of Isaac Newton discovering the force of gravity by an apple falling on his head is true or not. But it is likely that from such a simple event as this, Newton's Laws of Motion – the reason things move differently under certain conditions – became laid down. The apple falling on Newton's head certainly demonstrates the force of gravity, to which all objects on Earth are attracted. It is also likely to have happened between 1665 and 1666, when Newton had to leave Cambridge University because it had been closed due to the plague. Returning home to Woolsthorpe, he had time to think about things which interested him; for instance – gravity, the force which kept everything on the Earth, so that people, animals and objects did not float off into space. His father died in 1642, 3 months before Newton was born, and he inherited a vast area of land on which to breed sheep.

From the time of the discovery of gravity, humankind has taken great steps! Now it is possible to float in space … in the absence of gravity

But Newton soon showed he had no talent for farming. Shy and intelligent, Newton soon became known among the students at Grantham school for his amazing 'inventions' – water clocks, windmills, kites … In 1659 his mother persuaded him to abandon his studies and return home to work on his father's estate. But shortly after, thanks to an uncle, he entered **Trinity College, Cambridge**. From that moment, he made great strides, both in his studies and his fame. In 1669 he became a professor, having obtained the Chair in Mathematics at Cambridge and honours were soon being showered on him – such as Superintendent and then Director of the Royal Mint.

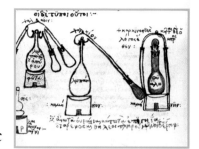

Some of Newton's filters and stills that he used as an alchemist in his search for the Philosopher's Stone

More than once, Isaac Newton was accused of being an alchemist (a sort of magician), and alchemists were not held in much respect. But such accusations did not prevent his being elected President of the **Royal Society** in 1703, and receiving a knighthood from Queen Anne in 1705 – the first scientist to have the honour of being knighted. Isaac Newton died at eighty four years of age.

Two births and two deaths

Anyone writing about Newton has problems establishing the date of both his birth and his death. According to some records, he was born on Christmas Day 1642; others say his birth was 4 January 1643. The same applies to the date of his death – 1726 or 1727? This difference is due to the **calendar** which was in operation. Until 1752, the **Julian** calendar, set out by Julius Caesar in the 1st century AD, was used in England, whilst, from 1582, the rest of Europe followed the **Gregorian** calendar introduced by Pope Gregory XIII. So, the English calendar set the year of Newton's birth as 1642, whilst according to the European calendar, it was ten days later, in 1643. In the case of his death, the reason for the difference between one date and the other is that, according to the English calendar, the year commenced on 25 March and not 1st January, so Newton died on the 20 March, and therefore in 1726!

Westminster Abbey, where Newton was buried

The silent inventor who illuminated the world with the battery

ALESSANDRO VOLTA
(Como 1745 – 1827)

In the deserted corridors of the National Institute of Science and Art in Paris, all that could be heard were the murmurs from inside the crowded lecture hall. Scientists and students had come from all over Europe to witness a demonstration of the latest invention in the field of electricity, the phenomenon of the age. Among the audience eagerly awaiting the arrival of the Italian inventor was the French Emperor, Napoleon Bonaparte. People began to get restless, their curiosity aroused by all that they had heard, and excited by the promise of what they would see and what would happen. Outside the auditorium a middle-aged man calmly approached the door. One short sigh was the only sign of any agitation on his part, before he turned the handle and entered. Going up to the desk, Alessandro Volta began his lecture, in front of him the invention about which he was to speak to all the scientists – the battery.

On the days of 7, 12 and 22 November 1801 people celebrated the achievement of Alessandro Volta in making the first battery, the first source of electrical energy. **Napoleon Bonaparte** had been so impressed by Volta's invention that in December of the same year, he awarded him a **gold medal**. Later, the French

Magdeburgo spheres, instruments used for experiments on vacuum

Emperor would also give Volta the sum of 6,000 francs plus the titles of Count, and Senator of the ancient Italian kingdom of Lombardy which was under French rule at the time.

Alessandro Volta was born in Como in 1745 into a noble and deeply religious family. Four of his brothers and sisters had taken vows of religion, but Alessandro did not want to do this. Instead, he studied subjects such as Latin and literature, before concentrating on science whilst still in his youth. In this, he was helped by a friend, Gattoni, who

An electrophore

prepared a science laboratory where Volta could work. According to family records, Alessandro Volta began to speak only when he was seven years old. Yet, by 1763, when he was eighteen years old, he had begun to write to famous European physicists and chemists about scientific matters. Two of the subjects about which he wrote were **methane**, the gas produced in swamps, and the construction of an instrument for building up **static electricity** by rubbing fur against it. Because of his writings and the interest which these caused, Volta won the financial support that he needed to study in Zurich, London and Paris a few years later. It was in Paris that Volta met researchers such as **Antoine-Laurent Lavoisier** and where he learned about the latest discoveries in the field of electricity. Returning to Italy, he became principal lecturer and then Rector of the University of Pavia. At this time, the kingdom of Lombardy had been very unsettled, first by being ruled by **Napoleon Bonaparte** and then the return of the reign of the Hapsburgs, the ruling house of Austria. But Alessandro Volta refused to take sides or voice his views, and because of this, he kept his position. When he died on 5 March 1827 at Como, twenty years had passed since he had worked with electricity. It was as if the battery itself had given one powerful charge and exhausted his energy for any further work in this field.

University of Pavia

Lecture Hall, University of Pavia, dedicated to Alessandro Volta

The battery

The invention of the battery came relatively late in 1800. After Volta's invention proved successful, other scientists – **Joseph Swan** and **Thomas Alva Edison** – later invented, quite separately, the first electric light bulb, so that the same electricity which had been produced by Volta's battery could begin to illuminate the wider world. By the time the scientist was 55 years old, he was known throughout Europe, due to other instruments he had invented for the study of the electrical phenomena – the **electrophore** for the production of static electricity, and the **eudiometer** for the combustion of gas by electricity. But nothing compared to the impact that he had made in the field of science with the invention of the battery, demonstrated at the beginning of the 19th century – a device composed of alternate discs of zinc and copper, with a pad soaked in acid between each disc, all connected by a copper wire. From this, the age of electricity took its first steps into history.

In stagnant waters

In swampy areas it is sometimes possible to see sudden bursts of flame above the surface. In ancient times this phenomenon came to be known as 'will-o'-the wisp' and it was thought to be a sign from the gods. People also believed it was the light from a lost soul, and its real origin remained unknown for many centuries. One important contribution to our understanding of this flame came from Alessandro Volta. In 1776, after a careful study of stagnant waters around Lake Como, he collected some methane. This is a gas given off by the remains of dead animals and plants as they rot at the bottom of the swamp. Volta discovered that, as the gas is released, it ignites and produces the flame. He demonstrated his theory by making a weapon which he called an **Eudiometric Pistol (also known as 'Volta's Gun')** which worked by the combustion (burning) of methane gas.

Galvani and his experiments on the legs of a dead frog

The discovery of Luigi Galvani (1737–1798) of electricity in animals (one experiment illustrated above) was ten years before Volta's invention of the battery. The biologist from Bologna was interested in the possible medical applications of electricity. He had noticed how the nerves and the muscles of dead frogs could move again when connected to metal wires. The numerous experiments carried out by Galvani were to demonstrate that animals and human beings had their own electricity and that the current applied by electrical sources could help and cure many illnesses and afflictions such as paralysis. Alessandro Volta contested Galvani's theory. He said that the

phenomena Galvani had reconstructed depended not on the skin tissue of the dead animal, but the metal wires being used in such a way that the electrical current passed through them. Volta's theory proved to be right.

In 1800, when Volta first demonstrated the battery, he likened his invention to the stingray (photograph above left), a fish with organs which could give an electric shock. The dissection of this animal revealed a remarkable similarity between the structure of its internal organs and the layers of metal discs and pads in Volta's battery.

Electricity in the plots of books

Studies on the phenomenon of electricity and in particular on its possible applications in the field of medicine also had a remarkable impact in the field of literature. In the novel *Frankenstein* written by the English author **Mary Shelley** in 1818, a mad scientist pushed himself to the very limits in trying to create life. Using parts of corpses dug up from a cemetery, he made a monster and subjected it to a powerful electrical charge. The effect was terrifying, because the horrible creature came to life, and in the end the monster rebelled against its creator. A similar plot was written ten years later by **Edgar Allan Poe** who was regarded as the forerunner of horror fiction. In *A Chat with the Mummy*, a spark is enough to bring a mummy back to life, with devastating results.

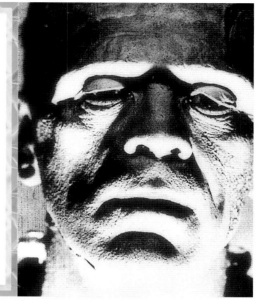

Frankenstein's monster

The first lamps were invented by both Joseph Swan and Thomas Alva Edison

Electricity moves on

The 17th century is often called 'the age of enlightenment'. This refers to the work of many scholars to defeat superstition and to promote the advance of knowledge – in fact, for people to live in the light. At that time, the only way to bring light into night-time darkness was to use candles and then gaslight.

Then the first pioneers in the use of electricity began to make real progress. The **lamp**, a real object of the electrical revolution, would arrive in the nineteenth century, and the first 'electric lights' would illuminate the rooms of buildings in the largest cities.

People also wanted to experience electric shocks to feel what it was like, and because some thought that it was good for the body. There was the so-called 'electric kiss', where a young man would put a hand on an instrument which produced electricity, such as a battery, then kiss a girl and the current would travel through her body and into the earth, rather like a lightning conductor.

New York by night. Here, the lights are so bright that they completely obscure the stars

*The self-taught inventor who led the
way in worldwide communication*

GUGLIELMO MARCONI

(Bologna 1874 – Rome 1937)

*The walls of the simple hut were lit only by the light from the road. At
the centre of the room, a small group of people were clustered
breathlessly around an instrument which looked rather like a telegraph
machine. Glancing out of an iced-up window, a man put his frozen hands
to his mouth, blowing on them for warmth. Another anxiously paced the
room making the hinges of the wooden door creak. Then, just when it
seemed that all hope was lost, a clicking sound signalled the arrival of
the message 'yellow time'. These two words meant only one thing:
the first transatlantic radio transmission had been a success. It
was enough to make everyone in the hut run outside and dance
on the ice despite temperatures of ten degrees below zero.*

On 12 December 1901, the letter S of the Morse Alphabet was transmitted across the Atlantic
Ocean. One year later, on 15 December 1902, a whole message was sent from Glace Bay in
Canada to Poldhu, England. The distance between these two stations was vast and the risk of
failure was high: but Guglielmo Marconi refused to consider defeat. Instead, he summoned all his
energy and his enthusiasm to carry out his experiment. Determination and a firm belief in his ideas
were both strong characteristics of this young inventor, born near Bologna in 1874. Although he
had no theoretical knowledge of physics (he had not even finished senior school) before he was
twenty years old, he had begun to carry out research into **electromagnetic waves**.

The team prepare for a transmission
experiment, Canada 1901

House where Guglielmo Marconi was born.

Marconi soon realized that this phenomenon could be an advantage in everyday communication. So, in 1895, he designed the first telegraph without wires ('wire-less' or radio telegraph) in history, using odds and ends and discarded materials. First, he carried out some experiments in the countryside around Bologna to make sure his 'wire-less' worked before demonstrating it. Then, in 1896 Marconi went to London, where, on 2 July 1897, he obtained the patent (registration of ownership) for his invention. In the same year, he founded his first company, the *Wireless Telegraph And Signal Company* and identified a possible application for his radio telegraph – the sea. At that time, the possibility of communication with the land would be an enormous advantage to shipping. Marconi began to concentrate his studies on the capacity of electromagnetic waves spreading out among the ocean waves, and converting these into radio signals. Once again, Marconi was successful. In 1899, messages began to be transmitted from one side of the English Channel to the other. This was followed by the foundation of a new company and more inventions, many of which were made possible by collaborators. For example, in 1905 **John Ambrose Fleming** introduced the thermionic valve, (sometimes called the Fleming valve) which was necessary for sound to be transmitted, and so this led to the invention of radio. Marconi became famous in a very short time, with the first **Nobel Prize for Physics** in 1909. But there were also attempts to discredit him, such as the so-called '**Marconi Scandal**', when he was accused of entering into secret agreements, although this was never proved. In the last years of his life, which ended in 1937, his commitment within scientific fields became less exciting. Leaving aside assistants and administrators he made mostly technical gadgets and concentrated on managing his companies. Marconi also began to make voyages aboard a ship which he had bought to use as a floating home: the **Elettra**.

Above, centre: electromagnetic oscillator

Right, Guglielmo Marconi completes some experiments with his 'wire-less' telegraph, helped by an assistant

SIGNAL FOR HELP

In 1838, the American inventor Samuel Morse (1791–1872) invented the telegraph machine. He also invented the Morse Code, an alphabet in which the letters are represented by dots and dashes. The international signal for 'help' – the famous SOS, is made up of three dots, three dashes and three dots.

MARCONI DAY

Between 1933 and 1934, Marconi made a journey around the world. During his travels, he attended Marconi Day, celebrated by organizations in the United States in honour of his discoveries.

The only significant dates in Marconi's adult life which were not connected with science and scientific matters were 1923, when he was accepted into the Italian Fascist Party, and 1936, when he defended Mussolini for declaring war against the African country of Ethiopia.

The ladder of success

Marconi was famous for two reasons – first, as a prolific inventor and second, as a clever businessman. In 1897, only one year into his patent of the 'wire-less' radio-telegraph (telegraph working by electromagnetic waves) he founded his first Wireless Telegraph And Signal Company, later re-named Marconi Wireless Signal Company.

It was the first of numerous business firms (by 1912, there were over thirty) and the prelude to a worldwide success.

He was received by monarchs, famous scientists (including Thomas Alva Edison, joint inventor of the electric light bulb) and even the Pope. In 1909, Marconi was awarded the Nobel Prize for Physics and a few years later, in 1912, he was knighted.

Marconi on board his luxury yacht *Elettra*

The Joy of Discovery

After the stuffiness and then the long, cold winter months spent in an attic, Marconi must have been looking forward to going out again into the open air of Bologna. But by the end of the summer of 1895, we can only imagine how anxious he must have been feeling. During the previous year, he had been testing various instruments that he had made to prove to himself that electromagnetic waves could travel considerable distances. Now, the moment of truth had arrived. The transmitter – the instrument which would send the message – (three dots, three dashes and three dots, corresponding to the letter S in the Morse Alphabet) was set up in the attic, and the receiver was ready, connected up in Pino, on the other side of a hill. The message was transmitted. There was a pause. Suddenly, the silence of the countryside was shattered by a loud bang. Marconi's brother Alfonso had been given the task of firing a rifle if the experiment worked. The shot that Marconi heard as he remained in the attic told him that his theory was correct. The message had been received.

The young Marconi with his first telegraph

Who invented the telephone?

The ten years between the end of the 19th century and the beginning of the 20th were marked by many important scientific discoveries. Scientists had to protect their inventions against the risk of being copied. But whereas Marconi was able to patent his invention, Antonio Meucci (1808–1889) could not afford the cost of patenting his important invention, the telephone. The long legal battle between Meucci and Alexander Graham Bell (1847–1922) who claimed ownership of the invention ended in 1885 with victory for Bell. It was only on 16 June 2002 that a debate on the whole matter took place in the American Congress, with the result that Meucci was given what he had always wanted in his lifetime – recognition as the inventor of the telephone. But this was little compensation, considering that the Italian inventor had died in poverty, using his last cent to try and prove the truth.

Above, bust of Antonio Meucci: right, Graham Bell tries out the telephone

Bell's electro-magnetic telephone

Escape from death

On 10 April 1912, the *Titanic*, a powerful transatlantic liner considered 'unsinkable' by its shipbuilders, sailed from Liverpool on its maiden voyage. Marconi should have been on board. He had been officially invited to cross the Atlantic Ocean on the *Titanic*, the pride of the shipping company, the White Star Line. But Marconi preferred to make his first journey to America aboard another liner, the *Lusitania*. This decision most probably saved his life. Four days into her voyage, the *Titanic* crashed into a giant iceberg and sank. Of two thousand people on board, only seven hundred lives were saved. Realizing the tragedy from which he had escaped, Marconi invented an instrument which would automatically transmit a radio signal for help in the event of danger.

Titanic

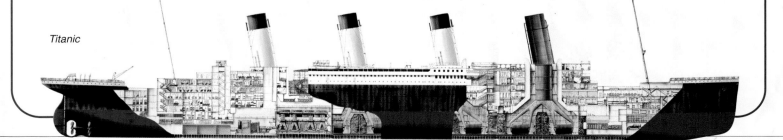

The engineering genius who designed and built tunnels, railways, bridges and steamships and whose work benefits so many people to this day

ISAMBARD KINGDOM BRUNEL

(Portsmouth 1806 – London 1859)

Brunel with the chains for the *Great Eastern*

The train was making good time. With each puff of steam came cheers from the crowds along the embankments, children smiling and waving flags. 'Long live the Prince! God bless Prince Albert!' Isambard Kingdom Brunel sat back in his seat, studying the handsome face of the husband of the young Queen Victoria. He knew every tree, every hedge, every road along the length of his Great Western Railway. Now, the royal train was approaching Bristol. There, Prince Albert would launch the 'SS Great Britain', the largest steamship ever seen and which Brunel had also designed and built. Gradually, the cheers became louder. From a distance there came the sound of a brass band ready to welcome him and the Prince.

Isambard Kingdom Brunel was one of the greatest engineers the world has ever known. Even as a small boy, Isambard had made up his mind that he would become a leading engineer, and by 1822, aged just sixteen, he began working for his father, **Marc Brunel** – a famous engineer and inventor. In 1825, Marc Brunel was given the task of building the **Thames Tunnel** under the river in **London from Rotherhithe to Wapping**. When his father became ill, Isambard was put in charge. Tunnelling with explosives proved very dangerous work. Isambard was seriously injured in an accident and had to hand back the task to his father. Fifteen years later the Thames Tunnel was completed. It is still in use today, as part of the East London Line on the London Underground. In 1833, Isambard Kingdom Brunel was appointed **Chief Engineer to the Great**

Clifton Suspension Bridge which crosses the Avon George, Bristol, England

Western Railway, building 118 miles (190 km) of railway line from **London to Bristol**. Within ten years, his design for the mighty **Clifton Suspension Bridge** to cross the **Avon Gorge at Bristol** had also been chosen – but this was not completed until 1864, five years after Brunel's death.

Tunnels

Building the Thames Tunnel (shown right) was an enormous task. It took eighteen years to complete, mostly because it cost far more than anyone had imagined. Many accidents and collapses too caused long delays. Brunel also built the famous **Box Tunnel**, near Bath. At over two miles (3.5 km) long, it was the longest tunnel in the world. Sadly, over one hundred men were killed during the five years it took to build.

Giant Steamships

The **Great Western** was the name of Brunel's first steamship, launched in 1837. This was the first ship to provide a regular service from England to America but the wooden ship caught fire. Brunel was now determined that this would not happen to his next ship. It would be made completely of iron. Like the **Great Western**, the **Great Britain** was the largest ship of all time. Now Brunel's ambition was to build a ship twice as large again – the biggest ever seen.

Alas for Brunel! The **Great Eastern** was so vast that it got stuck at its launch. It took many attempts and weeks of hard work by the shipbuilders before the huge ship was afloat – and there was still much to be done. Just days after work on the **Great Eastern** was completed, on 15 September 1859, Brunel died – many people believed through overwork. He left behind some of the greatest feats of engineering ever achieved, and which continue to benefit the lives of many people to this day.

Left and above SS Great Britain restored to its former glory in dry dock at Bristol

Bridges

The **Clifton Suspension Bridge** (above) was the most imaginative of all Brunel's bridge designs. The whole bridge is held up by chains and great iron rods (which is why it is called a 'suspension' bridge). Many people thought it would collapse but this famous bridge is still carrying travellers across the Avon Gorge over 140 years later. Brunel also built the famous **Royal Albert Bridge** at *Saltash* in Cornwall and the **Maidenhead Bridge** in Berkshire.

Railways – and docks

Brunel's Great Western Railway extended more than 1,000 miles (1,600 km), from London to Devon, Cornwall, Wales and parts of the Midlands. It was the most extensive railway in Britain and the largest in the world at the time.

Brunel also supervised the building of railways in Australia and India – and built two in Italy. Meanwhile, he had designed the Monkswear Docks at Bristol, followed by work on the docks at Milford Haven in Wales and at Plymouth in Devon.

The scientist, who, with the collaboration of her husband, discovered natural radioactivity

MARIE CURIE
(Warsaw, Poland 1867 – Sancellemoz, France 1934)

The young pupils filed through the door of the laboratory. It was the day for chemistry lessons and the teacher was none other than Marie Curie, the scientist who had discovered natural radioactivity. Nobody spoke as the scientist raised her eyes, looking around at her students one by one. Her gaze lingered on the face of her daughter Irene, so much like her, and looking at her mother with admiration. When the students were all gathered around the table, she made a sign for the curtains to be closed. In the darkness there glowed a tiny light in Marie Curie's hand. The 'magic' had happened, yet again. From the tiny fragments of radium which Marie Curie held, there glowed the intense light of radiation.

Marie and Pierre Curie

Marie Curie was both a scientist and a researcher who became famous for her studies on radioactivity. In 1907 she and her colleagues founded a '**co-operative school**' in which parent-scientists would take it in turns to educate their children. There were about ten children, including Irene, Marie's eldest daughter. The school lasted only two years, but it demonstrated how the role of scientists expands with the teaching and passing on of knowledge.

Marie Sklodowska was born in 1867 at Warsaw into a family of teachers. After finishing senior school, she took a job as a governess to earn money so that her sister Bronya could study medicine in Paris. In 1891 it was her turn to go to the French capital to enrol at the famous

Warsaw

university, the Sorbonne. In 1891, she graduated in science, and in 1894, in chemistry. In the same year in which she was awarded her second diploma she met her future husband and colleague, **Pierre Curie**. After they married in 1895, Marie began to carry out her own researches in Pierre's laboratory. In the meantime, he had been appointed lecturer at the School of Physics and Chemistry. For her qualifying paper, Marie Curie chose the analysis of radioactivity of **uranium**, a chemical element identified in 1896 by **Henri Becquerel**. In 1898, Marie Curie identified two new radioactive substances – **polonium** and **radium**. Although she received no money for this discovery (which would earn her and her husband their first Nobel Prize in 1903), Marie Curie continued to analyse samples of minerals from which to extract pure radium. In 1912, one year after winning her second Nobel Prize (which she won in her own right), she succeeded in registering with the International Commission on Radiological Units the measure of twenty two milligrammes of radium to establish the unit of measurement, the **curie** (in memory of

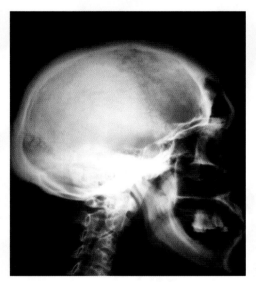

her husband who had died as the result of an accident in 1905). During the First World War, Marie Curie made further developments in her researches, using her own knowledge of radiation in hospitals on the battlefields, going to the front lines to carry out radiography to diagnose injuries in wounded soldiers. By the end of the War, her experiments had focused on the study of radiotherapy – the bombardment of cancer cells in the human body with radiation. Until just a few days before her death, Marie continued to handle the materials she had discovered, knowing that the radium to which she had been exposed had poisoned her body. She died from leukaemia.

Radiograph (X-ray) of a human skull

The discovery of radium took forty five months of uninterrupted analysis. An incredible physical as well as mental commitment was necessary in order to extract a little over .1 of a gramme of radium from around 500 kilogrammes of pitchblende (photograph, left).

*X-rays were discovered in 1895 by Wilhelm Conrad Röntgen (1845–1923). Whereas natural radioactivity is a property of atoms of some substances, Röntgen's X-rays were produced artificially through what came to be called the **cathode ray tube**.*

The Nobel Prize of 1903 was awarded to three people. As well as Pierre and Marie Curie, Henri Becquerel was also awarded the prize for the discovery of radioactivity in uranium.

The Poland of Maria Sklodowska

In Poland, the future Marie Curie, Maria Sklodowska, took part in the secret 'free university', reading Polish literature to other women. At that time, women were not allowed access to higher education. But Jadwiga Dawidowa, the man for whom she worked, was so impressed by the determination of his Russian governess (certain areas of Poland were then part of the Russian Empire) that he installed secret laboratories in his own home for the used of private students. One of these was Józef Boguski, a cousin of Maria, who had attended lessons given by the distinguished Russian scientist Dmitrij Mendeleev (1801–1907). Mendeleev was the man who had worked out the **periodic table of elements** – a table of the known chemical elements, sorted by how complicated the atoms are in each element. So, in a poorly-equipped research laboratory, Maria carried out her first scientific experiments.

The chemist Dmitrij Mendeleev

Pierre and Marie Curie in his laboratory

Marie Curie – Pioneer

Marie Curie was the first woman to be awarded a **Nobel Prize** (for physics) in 1903. She also had the honour, never before granted to a researcher, to study at the **Sorbonne**, the famous Paris university. In 1911 she achieved another significant goal, becoming the first scientist to be the sole winner of a second Nobel Prize, this time for chemistry. At that time, public recognition was almost totally limited to men, and she had to fight hard against prejudice. Assisting unpaid in the laboratory where her husband worked, she was at first excluded from being a candidate for the Nobel Prize. By the time her name was proposed for the second Nobel Prize, the general misgivings had diminished, at least from the scientific point of view. In 1921, she travelled to the USA, where she was invited to the White House by **President Warren G. Harding**. He presented her with a gram of radium on behalf of the American women who had collected enough money to buy it. This gift was especially valuable to Marie Curie, who needed all the radium she could get for her continuing researches. In 1922, she was made a member of the Academy of Medicine, famous all over the world for her work and her astounding achievements.

The Parisian University, the Sorbonne

Irene Curie with her mother in a research laboratory

Mother and daughter

Marie Curie often worked solely with her eldest daughter, **Irene**. Sharing a passion for scientific research and, in particular, an interest in radioactivity, their appearance was also very similar. They each dressed simply, often looking tired and with their hair ruffled. These two women dedicated their whole lives to science and in the end their work destroyed them (they both died from a serious form of leukaemia, caused by the exposure to radiation). During the First World War, they worked side by side in the development of a mobile radiology service, transporting equipment to carry out radiography for the benefit of wounded soldiers.

In 1935, Irene was awarded, together with her husband **Frédéric Joliot**, the Nobel Prize for Physics, just as her parents had been over thirty years before.

Polonium and Radium

It was in 1898 that radioactivity was defined as being the quality of some bodies to give off natural radiation. This field of physics was still experimental. The first discovery of radiation had been made only two years earlier, in 1896, by Henri Becquerel, during his studies on uranium. Few scientists seemed to understand the importance of continuing this research on other materials and substances, but Marie Curie did not share their views. She analysed a type of rock called pitchblende, and noticed that this produced more radiation than the same amount of uranium. She believed that pitchblende could contain new radioactive substances as well as uranium. In 1898, she discovered polonium (named after the country of her birth).

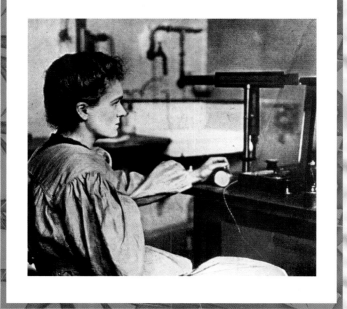

Irene Curie assisting her mother in her laboratory

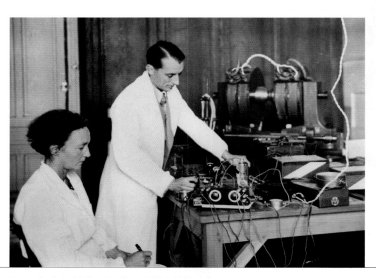
Irene Curie with her husband, Frédéric Joliot

*The strange physicist who astonished the world
with the introduction of his Theory of Relativity*

ALBERT EINSTEIN
(Ulm, Germany 1879 – Princeton, USA 1955)

*The day was like any other, with the staff at the Patents
Office in Bern, Switzerland, all at their places. At one
desk, almost completely buried beneath of a mountain of untidy papers, was a young man, just a
little over twenty years old. At home, he had left his young wife and his new-born son, but at that
moment, he hardly thought of them. The job at the Patent Office was a means of earning money –
but, that scarcely mattered, when his mind was totally absorbed by challenges and theories of
physics. It was difficult to work out a theory among stamps, registers and letters. But in time, he
managed to organize his ideas into a written text which could be understood. The time had come for
him to reveal his theory to the public.*

In 1905, Albert Einstein was still an unknown employee at the Patents Office in Bern. But at only
twenty six years old, he formulated his **Theory of Relativity**. During the following years, this theory
would revolutionize not only the scientific world, but also humankind's conception of the Universe.
Einstein's **General Theory of Relativity** maintained that gravity is a curved field in space and time,
curved by the presence of mass – and not a force, pure and simple, as Isaac Newton had said – so,
the greater the mass of an object, the more forcefully it will fall towards the Earth; whereas Newton
had said that all objects were attracted to Earth's gravity by the same force, no matter what the size
of the object or of what it consisted.
The scientist was born in 1874 in Ulm, Germany, into a family of Jewish merchants, who, in 1879
emigrated to Monaco. Here, Einstein's father and uncle set up a factory making electrical gadgets.
They soon decided to move the business to Italy, first to Milan
and then to Pavia, but Einstein remained behind to study
in Germany. But before long, Einstein left school and

The city of Ulm

rejoined his family. He had decided that he wanted to study mathematics and physics at the famous Zurich Polytechnic Academy. Whilst waiting to take the examination for admission to the University, Einstein went to the Swiss High School in Aarau. Switzerland was to become his country of adoption. In 1896 he was finally able to enrol at the Polytechnic Academy, where he graduated in physics in 1900. The Academy enabled Einstein to find his first job at the **Patents Office in Bern**. Although the professors at the Academy had not particularly encouraged the scientific ambitions of the new graduate, Einstein was soon in the habit of cutting working time to occupy himself in his studies.

Princeton University

His efforts and determination were rewarded in 1905 with the publication of five scientific papers. International recognition did not come immediately, but at least the door was open for him to teach at University. In 1909 he became lecturer in physics at Zurich. He had to wait until 1919 to become famous, when his **General Theory of Relativity** of 1916 was proved. This happened when members of the British Royal Society went to Guinea to study a **total eclipse of the Sun**. Einstein had predicted in 1911 that when this eclipse occurred, the Sun would appear to be very close to a certain star because the Sun's gravitational field would pull the star's light towards it, so making the star's light follow a curved path on its way to Earth.

After that, Einstein travelled all over the world – the USA (1921), Japan (1922), Palestine (1923). Whilst in Japan, he was awarded his first Nobel Prize. When **Adolf Hitler** came to power in 1933 and began his campaign against Jewish people, Einstein went to the USA, where he worked at the Institute for Advanced Studies of Princeton. During the last years of his life (he died in 1955), he spoke at numerous conferences in favour of peace and against the use of nuclear weapons in the event of war.

*A sculpture? A lighthouse? A tower? In fact, it is a solar observatory. Between 1920 and 1924 the so-called **Einstein Tower** was installed at Potsdam in honour of the German-born scientist.*

A *scientist who disappeared*

ETTORE MAJORANA
(Catania 1906 – ?)

Ettore Majorana was a pupil and colleague of the famous nuclear scientist **Enrico Fermi**. He was last seen on 25 March 1938 on a ferry boat leaving Palermo in Sicily, for Naples. The scientist, a Professor at the University of Parthenope, had been taking a day off in the Sicilian capital city. Sometimes, Majorana suffered fits of depression, often finding it difficult to go out of his house – and, on the advice of his friends and colleagues, he had decided to take a rest from his studies.

Quirino Majorana

Majorana was working on **physical theory**, a subject which required concentration and the ability to work alone. But having been brought up in a family of academics (an uncle, Quirino was a famous physicist), this was no problem. The chance to investigate more advanced scientific theories made him leave the Faculty of Engineering at Parthenope University in 1927 in order to join the group headed by **Enrico Fermi**. Majorana's natural solitude was already evident during those first years. He did not like being in the public eye – in 1931, he refused to deliver a paper on the energy of nuclear reactions, which would be revealed as being correct a few years later.

After a journey to Germany in 1933, his remoteness from his colleagues became even more evident. Going off to Naples, he spent a sleepless night at the Hotel Bologna, formulating theories in physics and mathematics. Many theories were put forward regarding his disappearance in 1938 – **suicide** (a possibility which was supported by two letters which he wrote), **withdrawal into a monastery**, and **fleeing** to a distant country. His body was never found and so nothing more is known.

The Sun Hotel at Palermo, where in 1938 the physicist Ettore Majorana stayed shortly before he disappeared.

The friends of via Panisperna

Starting from 1926 (the date of the arrival of Enrico Fermi at the Royal Institute of Physics in Rome), a villa at number **89 via Panisperna** was the meeting place for the leading Italian scientists in experimental physics. The atmosphere in the lecture rooms and in the laboratories was always electric. Each day brought forth new discoveries. These discoveries were analysed in informal lessons where everyone, from the latest arrival to the most famous researcher, worked closely together. Among themselves they used nicknames to indicate their roles in the group in a light-hearted way. Enrico Fermi was 'the father', his pupils Emilio Segrè and Edoardo Amaldi 'the occupants', and the President of the Institute, Mario Corbino, was called 'God the Father'. Majorana's name was 'the grand inquisitor', as if to underline his solitary and inquiring personality.

STRANGER THAN FICTION?
The author Leonardo Sciascia (1921–1989) wrote a book, 'The Disappearance of Enrico Majorana'. But the disappearance of the Sicilian scientist Enrico Majorana remains a mystery to this day.

Naturalists Chemists
and
Pioneers of Medicine

The wise doctor who set down the professional code for curing the sick

HIPPOCRATES

(Cos, about 460 BC – Larissa, about 370 BC)

In 429 BC, an atmosphere of death spread among the shadows of the temple of the Acropolis in Athens. All around were men, women and children, many of whom had fallen to the ground, shivering as the result of fever, their faces horribly disfigured and festering ulcers covering their bodies. The plague had spread from Beozia, north west of the city. Among this mass of misery, a doctor went around trying to cure as many people as he could, ignoring the danger of contracting the plague himself. As he examined the patients, he questioned them about their symptoms and their habits. Then he suggested some safeguards to stop the plague spreading further – burning the dead corpses, using ointments and isolating the sick. The doctor who with his 'cure' had established the code of medical practice did not flinch from his first and most important duty – that of helping each patient, even at the risk of his own life.

Hippocrates was born in 460 BC in Cos, a Greek island in the Aegean Sea. When he was only thirteen years old, he was allowed into the **Asklepieion**, or **Health Temple** of Cos, where he began learning to help sick people. Entering the temple to help the priest-doctor **Asclepius** (later to be created god of medicine) was an honour which was passed from father to son – and Hippocrates belonged to a family which had descended directly from Asclepius himself.

Even as a young man, Hippocrates' powers of observation clashed with the methods used by the

colleagues of Asclepius. He believed that a doctor's duty was to treat the whole patient and not just the apparent illness, trying to understand his or her customs and habits and carefully examining the entire body, instead of confusing the patient by praying to the gods and then explaining what they were supposed to have said. Before many years had passed, Hippocrates had left his family background, wanting to learn more about medicine and medical practice. He went to Egypt, where the priest-doctors had developed their own practice to a high level in the field of medical surgery. Returning to Cos in 438 BC, Hippocrates

An Egyptian occulist intent on curing a patient

committed himself to founding a **school of medicine** in the city, outlining a code of practice for the medical profession. This code included – respect for the rules of hygiene, talking with each patient in **isolation** rooms, a study of the surroundings and of the effect that the climate had on the patient. Hippocrates wrote about the effects of the relationship between the patient and his or her natural surroundings in his work *On Airs, Waters and Places*. Although he was often called to give consultations on rich and important people, Hippocrates always preferred to spend his free time in studying the habits of the ordinary people. His enquiring mind often compelled him to carry out long journeys to distant places, accompanied by his followers. The death of Hippocrates is shrouded in myth – but we do know that, in an age where the average life expectancy was around thirty years, he was about ninety years old when he died.

The fascination with women warriors

During one of his journeys, Hippocrates is said to have spent some time among the Scythians, a warlike population who lived in present-day Southern Russia. Hippocrates remained fascinated by the physical constitution of these warriors, who had to bear the strain of harsh conditions and unfavourable climates. He also paid particular attention to the **Amazons**, women who trained for battle, and where the mother of a young girl would remove her right breast, so as to make the use of the bow in archery easier.

Amazons in battle

Arsonist? Or fireman?

The one controversial event in the life of Hippocrates was when he was accused of being responsible for the **burning of the temple of Asclepius**. According to legend, some people testified to having seen him hurrying from the temple with the tablets of Asclepius. The writings on these tablets opposed the theories of Hippocrates. People also accused him of having copied the work of others. However, most of his fellow citizens interpreted the event differently. They maintained that Hippocrates had wanted to save the sacred tablets from disaster.

Hippocratic doctors at Galeno, in a fresco

A king in love

There are many stories about the work of Hippocrates – how he listened to and interpreted the words of his patients. One example is what happened when Hippocrates was called to Macedonia to cure **King Perdiccas**. The Court Physician had not been able to understand the cause of the illness which afflicted His Majesty. But Hippocrates just let the king speak freely of his past and his dreams. At the end of the consultation, it was clear to Hippocrates that Perdiccas was 'sick' with love for Fila, his childhood sweetheart.

Roman statue of Hygieia

A man becomes a god

The myth of Asclepius developed in the 5th or 6th century BC, at the same time as medical science and the practice of medicine was beginning in Greece. Until then, sick people and their families and friends could only pray to various gods. According to legend, Asclepius was the son of the nymph Coronis, who was a descendant of the kings of Thessaly, and the god Apollo. He was raised by the Centaur Chiron, who taught Asclepius the art of healing. He became a Greek hero, famous for his ability to heal. As time passed, this 'hero worship' meant that he was created a 'true' god. The children of Asclepius were often portrayed as his successors, with names which acquired meanings in the field of medicine – such as **Panacea**, meaning 'cure-all' and **Hygieia**, goddess of health. It is from her name that we get the word 'hygiene', meaning the practice and maintenance of good health.

Hippocrates visits
a patient

The cure and the Code of Practice

As well as a modern vision of medicine, Hippocrates left a professional teaching, based on careful observation of the patient and his/her surroundings. In his code, seen as part of his cure, Hippocrates set out the moral rules which every doctor must follow in the practice of his/her profession.

- The obligation to **pass on the knowledge** they have acquired to colleagues and students to enable them to achieve the same cure, so as to advance the progress of medicine.

- The commitment to do one's best in every way to **cure every patient**.

- The duty not to use any substance or treatment which could injure or harm the patient.

- The respect for **professional confidentiality**. The doctor must not divulge to other people what he/she has seen or heard during a visit to a patient.

The 'god' Asclepius
with a patient

Sayings of Hippocrates

In the *Corpus Hippocraticum*, said to be written by Hippocrates (but which contains some work by his students), there is an important section on *Aphorisms*, which contains around 406 sayings. These are written almost in a light-hearted way, almost like sentences which have been inserted into other writings of Hippocrates, but they are easy to remember and make good sense, even in today's modern world.

* *Nature is the only thing able to heal.*

* *All is human and all is divine.* Nature, given by the gods, supervises each human aspect, therefore everything which surrounds human beings is a holy manifestation.

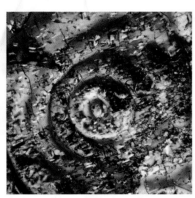

* *Life is short, skill is longer.* Natural phenomena, such as a human life, develops rapidly, whilst medical skill progresses slowly.

* *Extreme illnesses, extreme remedies.* To conquer serious illness, doctors may use extreme methods of treatment, where necessary.

Doctors and medical students still refer to the ancient term 'the Hippocratic Face' which is assumed to indicate that a patient is near to death.

An image seen through a microscope

Above, Hippocrates among the plants. He was the first to realize the medical properties of the willow bark, from which we get acetylsalicylic acid (aspirin)

Democritus, the 'laughing philosopher'

As Hippocrates grew old, he was often depicted as a man who was tormented by the idea of having failed to reach all his true aims in helping the sick and not to have succeeded in curing suffering humanity. According to legend, the old doctor was summoned to Rhodes to cure the philosopher Democritus (below, with Heraclitus in a fresco by Donato Bramante). Democritus was known as the 'laughing philosopher' and his habit of bursting into laughter for no reason was generally seen as a clear sign of madness. But Hippocrates soon saw that the man's strange behaviour was his way of expressing contempt for what he saw as 'madness' in others. In fact, Democritus was a very wise and a very clever person.

As they spoke together, Hippocrates saw that Democritus had fully understood something which he had not – the fact that no person could be expected to live forever, therefore no person could always be saved from the results of illness. Only nature was everlasting, therefore only nature could cure in the end.

The brilliant experimenter who made chemistry a scientific discipline

ANTOINE-LAURENT LAVOISIER

(Paris 1743 – 1794)

Men, women and children crowded together, thrilled to be present at the sight of another execution following the French Revolution. This was a special day. Not only aristocrats would mount the scaffold, but also the hated members of the 'Ferme Général', who had collected high taxes from the French people for the king. From the top of the guillotine, the blade slid to the bottom, taking off the head of the condemned man. The crowd cheered. Only one woman, in despair, looked away from the terrible sight. Her eyes, wet with tears, were fixed on a man who calmly awaited his turn.

The man awaiting execution was Antoine-Laurent Lavoisier, who would later be recognized as the 'father of chemistry'. The young woman was Marie-Anne Pierrette Paulze, wife and co-worker of the French scientist. During the period of the so-called **Terrors** following the outbreak of the French Revolution (1789) nobody was exempt from the judgement of the revolutionary Tribunal. Nor could anyone appeal against their decision. So, on 8 May 1794, the head of Lavoisier, a member of the Tax-Collecting Agency *Ferme Général* fell in the Place de la Revolution in Paris (now, Place de la Concorde).

Born in 1743 into a rich Parisian family, Lavoisier enrolled at a very young age at the Collège Mazarin, where he studied literature and language, as well as mathematics and many fields of science, such as astronomy and botany. However, chemistry was his passion, at that time a 'mixture' of medical practice and a belief in alchemy – seen as a sort of 'magical' ability to convert base metal into silver. But Lavoisier saw chemistry as a more serious field of science in its own right and he soon began conducting experiments to demonstrate chemical phenomena, his findings set down in specific terms relating to the elements, properties and reactions of materials observed in his laboratory. In 1763, Lavoisier graduated in law. But, instead of taking up a legal career, he left on a series of journeys to carry out research. By the time he returned, he had acquired an amazing knowledge of botany, meteorology and geology. These studies, and in

Siege of the Bastille

particular, a special way of cataloguing minerals and plants, would be used by Lavoisier to establish a new approach to chemistry. 1768 was a crucial year in the life of the scientist. First, he was admitted as a member of the **Académie Royale de Sciences**, an institution which numbered among its members the finest French researchers. Second, he bought a contract for the collection of taxes, becoming a member of the institution the **Ferme Général** which, according to the ordinary people, became rich at the expense of the poor. Lavoisier regretted this decision many years later, in 1794, when he was condemned by the Revolutionary Tribunal for having contributed to the suffering of France and the French people by fraudulent collection of taxes. At his death, Lavoisier left behind a precious heritage – a new language specifically for chemistry (*Methods of Chemical Nomenclature*) and a paper in which he described most clearly phenomena such as respiration, oxydization and combustion, as well as the characteristics of numerous elements, such as oxygen, hydrogen and water.

Hydrostatic balance

A financier and a chemist

The Ferme Général was a tax-collecting agency. Its members were often seen to use dishonest methods in the collection of taxes, which is why they were so despised by the poorer people. But in his role of tax collector, Lavoisier was always honest, although, due to his senior position, he was able to use some of the revenue he collected to equip his own laboratory with the latest instruments. During a journey in Alsace and Lorraine, he spent the equivalent of 16,000 Euro to buy over one hundred books. But he made his biggest mistake in 1787, when he was advised to build a city wall around Paris to try and stop illegal traffic between the city and the countryside. This was so unpopular and caused so much resentment among the population, that it would become a significant factor when the Tribunal decided to sentence him to death.

The experiment, painted by Joseph Wright 'Wright of Derby'

The meticulous naturalist who revealed through his theory the Origin of the Species

CHARLES DARWIN

(Shrewsbury 1809 – Downe 1882)

The ship pitched and tossed on the sea, the wind rustling through the billowing sails. The members of the crew, their faces browned by the Sun, muscles toughened by hard work, busied themselves bolting down the hatches and attending to the rigging, the captain keeping a close watch on all that was going on. He noticed a young man alone at the stern, eyes fixed on the land as it receded further and further into the distance, those islands which had become so important to him and which had led to his theories, becoming veiled in a mist from the sea. Ahead lay a long voyage home to England, at the mercy of the ocean. After that there would be weeks of cataloguing all the species of animal and plant life which he would be bringing back, and writing down his own theory of evolution. But now his eyes were still turned in the direction of the Galápagos Islands, the extraordinary world which nature had endowed with so many different shapes, colours and perfumes.

Charles Darwin spent about one month between September and October 1835 on the Galápagos Islands. It had been only a short exploration, compared with the complete voyage of *The Beagle* which had been commissioned by the British Admiralty. The aim was to survey the east and west coasts of South America and the Pacific Islands, with the main purpose of taking a series of highly accurate records of their positions in order to improve the British naval charts of those parts of the World. So, before landing on the Galápagos Islands, Darwin had spent years exploring South America, as well as the coasts of Australia and Africa.

The whole journey was supposed to have lasted only two years. Instead, it lasted over five years.

The Beagle in full sail

The Beagle

Charles Darwin was born in 1809. His father and grandfather were both doctors, and Charles was expected to follow in the family tradition. However, he had to give up medical studies, because he could not stand the sight of blood. So, he enrolled at Cambridge University to study religion, with the idea of becoming a clergyman. At Cambridge, he met John Steven Henslow, a scientist and botanist, as well as a clergyman, and it was Henslow who got Darwin the job of unpaid naturalist on board *The Beagle* in 1831. By then, Darwin was twenty two years old, with a passion for collecting rocks, coins and stamps. By the time he returned home, he had given up all thoughts of a Church career. Instead, he devoted himself to analysing

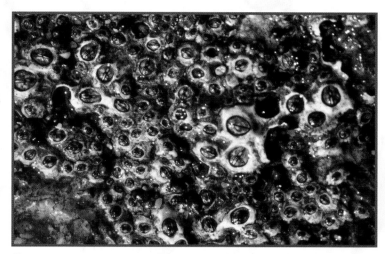

Cirripedes, molluscs studied with particular attention by Darwin

every detail of the notes he had made during the entire voyage of *The Beagle* and the time spent on the Galápagos Islands, as well as the identification of samples he had collected, such as fossils, leaves and minerals. In 1842, he moved to Downe in Kent, where he settled with his wife, a cousin, whom he married in 1839. There, he worked on his main theory of **evolution** – how all living things change and develop according to their surroundings. He also investigated animal emotions, both by carrying out experiments and through observations (in particular, the way in which

animals care for their young). The only obstacle to his research was a succession of illnesses from which he suffered all his life. Darwin wrote his theories in a book *The Origin of The Species*, published in 1883, the year in which he died. Even then, Darwin was still occupied with clearing the doubts and unanswered questions which persisted in his mind.

Darwin represented as a monkey in a cartoon

A fierce defender

On 30 June 1860 at Oxford University a heated argument took place between **Thomas Henry Huxley**, a close friend of Darwin who supported his theory of evolution, and a representative of the Church of England, Bishop **Samuel Wilberforce**. The Bishop fiercely attacked Darwin's theory of evolution, asking Huxley if he had been descended from a monkey through his mother or his father. Huxley answered that he would rather have had an ape for a grandfather, than a man who used his great intellect for the purpose of introducing ridicule into a serious scientific argument (obviously a reference to Wilberforce).

The transformation of animals

Over the centuries, living things have changed continually altering as certain characteristics happen to favour their survival better than others – this is the summary of Darwin's Theory of Evolution and the basis on which he wrote his book *The Origin of the Species*. This does not mean, as has often been thought, incorrectly, that the giraffe's neck has become longer through the poor animal continually trying to reach the leaves at the top of the tree. In fact, the evolution of the giraffe has been determined by that which is often defined as '**the survival of the fittest**'. Only those species with the longest necks succeed in feeding themselves and keeping alive, to reproduce and so pass on the right genes (hereditary characteristics). But the course of a natural genetic modification, or natural change, takes a long time and happens through gradual stages. This demonstrates what has been termed '**rings of existing conjunctions**' in animals which retain features of their original structure. The Duck-Billed Platypus, for example, is a mammal (the female feeds her young with her own milk), yet lays eggs, just like its reptile ancestor!

Female duck-billed platypus with her eggs

A NAME FOR EVERYTHING

Plants and animals, still living or extinct for thousands of years, are classified by two names, both in Latin; the first, a noun beginning with a capital letter, signifies the genus; the second, an adjective written all in small letters, signifies the species. For example – the common green frog – for the genus we write Rana *(meaning frog) and for the particular species* esculenta, *which describes it. The inventor of this system of cataloguing was the Swedish naturalist Carolus Linnaeus (1707-1778).*

Carolus Linnaeus in a portrait by J. H. Scheffel

TRUE GIANTS

When Darwin saw the giant land turtles moving slowly among the thick vegetation, he honoured them with the name of their island home. Galápagos in fact means 'the large turtles'.

Robert Fitzroy,
Commander of *The Beagle*

DARWIN AND PLANTS

It was Darwin who first noticed that the most brightly-coloured plants are those which need to attract insects in order to be fertilized. He also observed how flowers of the same plant were often very different, due to cross-pollination by bees transferring pollen from one flower to another. His theory proved correct, and in 1877, he published his findings in 'The Different Forms of Flowers on Plants of the Same Species and Effects of Cross and Self Fertilization in the Vegetable Kingdom' published in 1877.

Long ago, seals had legs. But by evolution, these have been transformed into flippers

A World Almost Completely Isolated

The Galápagos are a group of nineteen islands in the Pacific Ocean. They were discovered in 1535 by the Bishop of Panama, **Fray Tomás de Berlanga** and became part of Ecuador in 1832. The Galápagos Islands have always been outside the routes of navigators and conquerors, which is why they have kept their unique fauna (wild life) and flora, with species sometimes incredibly different from one island to another. It was Darwin who unwittingly ended this long isolation. When his theories became famous and the results of his observations became widely known, the Galápagos became almost like an open air, natural laboratory, where serious researchers and the simply curious gather from all over the world. The danger of ruining the balance of nature has made it necessary to introduce strict regulations on the number of visitors and on the rules of conduct that must be obeyed with regard to the animal and plant-life. As well as safeguarding the wild life on the Galápagos, these measures have been taken in order to prevent a repeat of what happened between 1811 and 1844, when over 15,000 turtles disappeared from the islands, shut up in the pens of ships to provide food for the crews.

The gardener monk who discovered genetics by studying pea plants

GREGOR MENDEL

(Heinzendorf 1822 – Brno 1884)

The shades of twilight fell across the deserted courtyard. In the light of the setting Sun, the tops of the trees and the glass of the greenhouses seemed like glowing embers. The old monk, sitting heavily on the chair, closed his eyes and listened. From a distance came the dull buzz of the bees, then the echo of a storm brewing. He needed to sort out his thoughts. Almost too tired to move, he had retreated into the monastery garden to be alone, his mind still occupied with the research he had carried out. The results were there for all to see, but nobody had yet understood his work. Perhaps, one day…

Pea plant flower

When he died in 1884, Gregor Mendel was the **Abbot** of the Monastery of San Tommaso at Brünn (now Brno). The year before, when he was a simple **monk**, Mendel had carried out some botanical experiments on **the plants of peas**, but nobody had understood the importance of his discovery. It was only in the 20th century that scientists realized that his studies had led to the science of genetics. Born in 1822 in a village of Moravia, Austria (now part of the Czech Republic) to a family of humble peasants, Mendel had the chance of studying at the school in Heinzendorf for the sons of farm-workers, which is where he developed his passion for botany. In 1845, he entered the Augustian monastery in Brünn. There, he continued his studies, and thanks to the Abbot, Cyril Napp, he spent a good deal of his free time in the garden and in the greenhouses. Despite two failed attempts to enrol at university in 1850 and 1856, he succeeded in being appointed as a tutor at the University of Vienna. Following this, he worked as a teacher in charge of the High School of Brünn from 1854 to 1868. Until his death, Mendel developed numerous interests – the care of the garden, **apiculture** (bee-keeping), **meteorology** and **playing chess**. But in his final years, the time he spent on science was reduced, due to the duties he had to carry out as Abbot.

Cross-breeding peas

In 1854, the monastery of San Tommaso was at risk of closure. The bishop had discovered that the Monk Mendel had carried out 'immoral' research – mating grey and white mice to see what colour their babies would be. The danger passed, because Mendel decided to continue his experiments with plants, in particular *Pisum sativam* (the pea plant).

But, what could be so interesting about peas? It had taken years to discover it, but at last the incredible patience of the monk was rewarded. He understood that there existed **dominant characteristics** which were passed on directly from parent to child and other, **recessive characteristics**, which can develop in successive generations. For example – a husband has blue eyes, his wife has brown. Their son is born with brown eyes (the dominant characteristic) whilst the grand-daughter has blue eyes, like her grandmother (recessive characteristic).

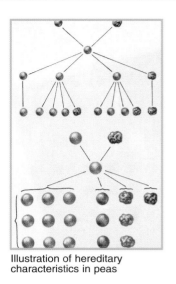

Illustration of hereditary characteristics in peas

Genetics in brief

The expression 'you are what you eat' is true up to a point. Nutrition does play an important role in the development of a human being. But there are other factors which cannot be altered simply by a change in diet. The colour of eyes, the hair ... these are part of our cultural heritage (**genome**) and as such remain unchanging (even if a person uses coloured contact lenses!) All this information (**genes**) is contained in one's **DNA** (Deoxyribonucleic Acid) the substance which forms the **chromosomes** – stick-like filaments in which the nucleus of each cell is found.

Experiments on genetic modification of vegetables

Drosophila, commonly known as the 'Vinegar Fly' seen through a microscope

FROM PEA PLANTS TO FLIES

At the beginning of the 20th century, the American biologist Thomas Hunt Morgan abandoned his research on the hereditary characteristics of plants in order to concentrate on one insect – the Drosophila (fruit fly family), which can sometimes produce young that have major differences to the parents. For example, Morgan found that some flies with red eyes laid eggs that hatched into white-eyed young.

Two men and one woman

In 2003, after two years of waiting, the results of the **Human Genome Project** were announced. This project would be the means of providing a complete 'map' of genes – about 20,000 are present in the DNA of a human being. Fifteen years had passed from the time when James Watson and Francis Crick published in the journal 'Nature' (25 April 1953) their amazing discovery: the structure of DNA. Part of the merit must go to Rosalind Franklin (1920-1958), a scientist who, in 1946, took X-ray photographs of biological molecules. In photograph number 51, it is clearly seen that the DNA consists of a double filament in the form of a helix (spiral), thus proving an important part of the theory of Watson and Crick.

James Watson

The hard-working chemist who transformed medicine by discovering germs

LOUIS PASTEUR

(Dôle 1822 – Villeneuve-l'Étang 1895)

On the laboratory table there were curious-looking flasks with short necks, a microscope, distilling equipment ... Through the windows could be heard the wild howls of dogs in the garden. A child, looking rather frightened by the tense atmosphere, made his way hesitantly towards the centre of the room where a chair sat ready for him. All eyes were on his face. Time seemed to stop, as an assistant carefully prepared the injection. The faces of the onlookers were anxious, everyone holding their breath. Louis Pasteur stood silently in a corner of the room, calmly confident that the injection would conquer the terrible disease of rabies. He knew that the little boy, Joseph, would not die.

Louis Pasteur was born in Dôle, France, in 1822, the same year in which Gregor Mendel was born. Apart from the date of their birth, nobody would link the timid Austrian botanist with the famous French chemist, except for them both dedicating their lives to scientific research. At first, Pasteur seemed be more interested in the arts; at a young age, he painted family portraits and landscapes of local views. But despite his talent as an artist, it was science in which he enrolled at the École Normale Supérieure, the famous teaching college in Paris. Here in 1847, he obtained the title Doctor of Chemistry. In the course of his studies in chemistry, he carried out many observations and experiments

Pasteur in his laboratory

with a microscope and this led to his becoming more interested in biology. In 1854, he became Professor at Lille University, where he completed a study on **fermentation** (a chemical phenomenon which, for example, transforms the **bacterial culture** of yeast in wine).

Pasteur discovered that the process of fermentation was due to the action of bacteria, micro-organisms which also cause infection and illness. This discovery encouraged Pasteur to widen his own research, first within the animal kingdom and then in human beings. In 1865, he went to the south of France to deal with the problems caused when silkworms were hit by an epidemic, so that no silk was being produced. In 1877, he studied and defeated cholera in hens, and in 1885, he created a system of vaccination against rabies (a fatal disease carried by dogs and wolves). When he died in 1895, he was the most famous French scientist, the founder of a new discipline, microbiology.

In a glass of beer

Most of the discoveries carried out by Pasteur came about as an answer to numerous practical problems which were brought to his notice from time to time. For instance, in 1854 he was asked to explain the reasons for the souring of alcohol as a result of the action of sugar beet. In 1865, he resolved the problem of silkworms being killed by disease; and in 1870, he offered his help to French brewers to gain an advantage over the producers of German beers. The reason for so many problems which afflicted French agriculture, Pasteur discovered, were **microbes** (germs). Microbes were invisible to the naked eye, but he could see them clearly under the microscope, discovering how they multiplied, how they lived and how they could be killed. In the course of his studies, Pasteur established that germs could be found everywhere and anywhere, and that they are the cause of illness and disease.

In 1886, Pasteur was spending a lot of time on parties and receptions. His purpose was to attract funding for the construction of a laboratory. On 14 November 1888, the results of his efforts were seen in the **Pasteur Institute** *in Paris. To this day, the Pasteur Institute is committed to the research of infectious illnesses.*

From Pasteur ... pasteurisation
Every morning when we wake, we can enjoy our breakfasts with milk in complete safety, thanks to Pasteur. He invented the system of pasteurisation, where the milk is brought to a boiling point of about 100°C (212°F) and in the absence of air, to eliminate all germs.

Rabies

During the Second World War, the old custodian at the Pasteur Institute lost his life when the Germans who had occupied Paris, succeeded in entering the crypt where Pasteur and his wife were buried, despite the man trying to stop them. This man was **Joseph Meister**, the young boy who, in

1885, had been cured of rabies, thanks to the vaccination administered by Pasteur. Joseph was the first in a long series of people hit by this illness who responded successfully to the experiments of Pasteur. (Photograph shows a group of men and women who had been cured of Rabies).

The Franco-Prussian War

Pasteur was in almost constant conflict with two German scientists, Justus von Liebig, the chemist who had created an effective system to conserve meat (beef extract) and Robert Koch, the doctor who identified the bacteria which caused tuberculosis and cholera. The reasons were not only scientific, but also political. The main reason was the enmity between France and Germany, resulting in 1870 in the Franco-Prussian War which ended with a victory for the Germans. With the outbreak of hostilities, Pasteur refused an honorary degree which had been conferred on him in 1868 by the University of Bonn for his discoveries in the medical field.

Robert Koch

The woman who sacrificed her life for the mountain gorilla

DIAN FOSSEY

(San Francisco 1932 – Rwanda 1985)

On 26 December 1985, the researcher Dian Fossey who lived in the volcanic mountain region of Virunga, east-central Africa, was found dead in her hut, killed by the blows from a machete. Her killer has never been found.

She had arrived in Africa nineteen years before, in 1966 in Rwanda to study the behaviour and the habitat of the mountain gorilla in the middle of a six-month programme to register the number of gorillas present in the area. She remained there for nineteen years, until her brutal death.

Dian Fossey was not qualified in animal behaviour, but she was spurred on by a great passion which she had developed as a girl. When she arrived for the first time in Africa, she brought her training and experience as a children's occupational therapist, which also helped her to understand the behaviour of mountain gorillas. In her daily contact with the **gorilla**, Dian Fossey deepened her knowledge of relationships between examples of the same species, noticing that the gestures and behaviour of primates (apes) are extraordinarily similar to those of humans. It was only in 1974 that she obtained a degree in Zoology from Cambridge University.

The battle continues

Dian Fossey created the Digit Fund, an association for the protection of the mountain gorilla, in memory of Digit, a male gorilla, killed by game poachers. She had established a particular relationship with this gorilla and so was broken-hearted when she found his body.

In 1992, the foundation changed not only its name to the Dian Fossey Gorilla Foundation, but also its aims. As well as the campaign for the guardianship of primates, it also gives help to the population of Rwanda, who are unsettled by unending battles between two ethnic groups, the Hutu and the Tutsi.

Tribal dance of the Tutsi

The actress Sigourney Weaver in a scene from the film-documentary **Gorillas in the Mist** *(1988) based on Dian Fossey's autobiography.*

PRINCES KINGS and EMPERORS

Rameses II riding a war chariot

The pharaoh who fought the Hittites and built beautiful temples in Egypt

RAMESES II

(circa 1304 BC – circa 1224 BC)

Many soldiers in the army were too terrorized to fight. Others were still a long way from the place of conflict, the plain of Kadesh. The hope of victory was hanging by a thread, but the pharaoh, upright in his chariot of war, would not surrender. Surrounded by angry crowds of the enemy Hittites, Rameses II could count only on his personal guard and his own courage. Six times he had ordered his men to attack the enemy. But he was the one, the earthly being of a god, who launched himself into battle beside his troops, firing arrows to slaughter the Hittite soldiers.

In the spring of 1274 BC, the fifth year of the reign of Rameses II, there was a great battle between the Egyptian and the Hittite armies on the plain of **Kadesh**, an ancient city of Syria.

The pharaoh, tricked by information from two messengers, spies sent by the enemy king **Muwatalli** had to fight with a much smaller army than that of the enemy. The bravery of Rameses, combined with help from an Egyptian division which came unexpectedly from the rear, changed the course of the whole battle, and it ended with a temporary suspension of hostilities. And so, for the second time, Rameses II had to return to Egypt without having conquered the Syrians. When he was about fifteen years old and reigned on the Egyptian throne together with his father, Pharaoh **Seti I** he had already fought the Hittites at Kadesh. On that occasion, too, the conflict had ended with neither victory nor defeat. After the battle which Rameses II had fought as sole pharaoh in 1274 BC, the relationship between the Egyptian and the Hittite kingdoms remained hostile. Then in 1259 BC, a lasting peace settlement between the two people was created – a peace treaty between Hattasuli III, the Hittite sovereign who had taken the place of Muwatalli and Rameses II. This was the first international agreement in history!

Colossus of Rameses II

After the wars which he had fought during the first part of his reign, Rameses II dedicated himself, like no other Egyptian sovereign before or after him, to the construction of great monuments, such as temples, tombs, burial chambers and statues. For the rest of his long life (it is thought that he died at over eighty years of age) he carried out many important works which survive thousands of years later. On the walls of his Ramesseum (an enormous funeral temple), on the great sanctuary of Abu Simbel and on the ancient temples of Karnak and Luxor, he had carved in hieroglyphic characters the story of his life, his heroic undertakings and the events of his family.

Inside the Ramesseum

The famous sons of Rameses II

Symbols on the walls of the tomb of Khaemuwaset

Rameses II had many wives who bore him a great number of children (it is thought about a hundred, including boys and girls). Many died at a young age, but others accompanied their father, either on military campaigns or carrying out official duties. Only two names have been recorded - Merneptah and Khaemwaset, both born of Istnofret, the second wife of the Pharaoh, and they left their mark in the history of Egypt. Merneptah was the one who survived Rameses II and inherited the throne, becoming pharaoh in 1224 BC. Khaemwaset did not have the same good fortune. But although he died before Rameses II in about 1235 BC and had no royal title, he became more famous than his brother. He became priest of the god Ptah, and when he was just over twenty years old, he began restoring ancient burial sites and committed himself to the religion of sacred bulls (Hapi). We know that he cleaned surfaces with sand and restored ancient monuments, such as the grand pyramid of Cheopes at Giza, demonstrating a passion similar to that of modern archaeologists.

Funereal temple of Rameses II

*The Frankish king who founded
the Holy Roman Empire*

CHARLES V (CHARLEMAGNE)
(Ghent 748 – San Jerónimo de Yuste 814)

*On a cold Christmas morning in 800, people had gathered in
the Basilica of Saint Peter in Rome to attend Mass. Most of
them had arrived a few days earlier to support Pope Leo III,
who had been threatened by a plot of Roman nobles. The King
of the Franks (the kingdom of what is now northern France,
Belgium and western Germany) was present. Shortly before the
most solemn moment of the Mass, the Pope lifted a crown and
placed it on the head of the king. At this, everyone cried out three times,
'To Charlemagne, crowned by God great emperor to bring peace, life and victory!'
Pope Leo then knelt before the new Roman Emperor, Charlemagne.*

Charlemagne receiving the philosopher Alcuin

On Christmas Day 800, Charlemagne, already king of the Franks and
the people of the ancient Italian kingdom of Lombardy, was
proclaimed Roman Emperor. This was his reward for supporting
Pope Leo III, when a group of the Roman nobility wanted to take
over the political role of the Pope.

Charlemagne, born on 2 April 748, became King of the Franks at
only twenty years old, in 768, following the death of his father **Pepin
III**. But until 771 his kingdom was limited to half the Frankish
territory, because his younger brother Carloman reigned over the
other half. Following the death of his brother, and after he had united the two
halves of the kingdom, Charlemagne launched a military campaign against the
Saxons (a Germanic tribe) with the aim of widening the borders of his realm
to the east. The conquest of this zone would prove to be long and difficult,
occupying his army on and off for over thirty years. Then in 773 he was
forced to undertake another campaign, this time against the
Italians. The Pope, **Adrian I** had asked for his help against the
King of Lombardy, **Desiderius**, who had invaded papal
domains. After a long siege around Pavia, the capital city of
Lombardy, from the autumn of 773 to the summer of 774, Charlemagne
defeated Desiderius and was crowned King of Lombardy. But the battle
against the Moslems in Spain in 778 ended in a disastrous failure. A
section of Charlemagne's troops were slaughtered by the

The cross of Desiderius

Coronation of Charlemagne

Basques (the people living in the Pyrenees, the mountain chain between France and Spain) whilst he was on his way home. The positive outcomes were the military campaigns against the Bavarians commanded by Tassilo III and also against the Avars, ending in 795 with vast regions of the land of the River Danube becoming part of Charlemagne's realm. When he became Emperor, Charlemagne had to work hard in the organization of a kingdom which, as the result of one conquest after another, had become more and more extensive. As well as creating a **palace school** for the instruction of administrators, he also entrusted parts of his original kingdom to men in his confidence, making them Marquesses and Earls. The co-ordination and communication between the outer zones of Charlemagne's realm and his court was carried out by messengers travelling across the country. To avoid battles breaking out between his sons after his death, he issued in 806 the *Divisio regnorum* (division of kingdoms), the document which defined the duties and the titles given to each son. When Charlemagne died on 28 January 814, just one son inherited his kingdoms – **Louis ('The Pious')** who had survived his brothers and in 813 been proclaimed Emperor, alongside his father.

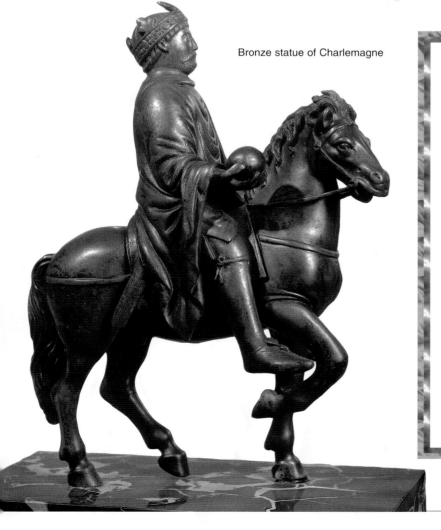
Bronze statue of Charlemagne

Saxon Resistance

The war fought by Charlemagne against the Saxons (a pagan tribe from Saxony, part of what is now Germany) was long and bloody. It began in 772 with the conquering and destruction of a place of Saxon culture – the **Igdrasil**, a pillar which Saxons believed supported the world. This conflict finally came to an end after thirty years of bloodshed, in 804. To overcome the resistance of the Saxons, Charlemagne used every method he could, both political and military, often demonstrating a cruel streak. For example, in 782, in the locality of Verden, he condemned to death, in one day, 4,500 Saxons. Not even the submission of the Saxon king **Widukind** who was baptized in the church at Attigny on 25 December 785, and the passing of severe laws could make Charlemagne absolutely certain that this proud German people would remain under his control. The lengthy conflict ended only in 804, after one last campaign to put down a revolution in the land of the River Elba, when the Saxons finally surrendered.

The fierce warrior who became
emperor of the Mongols

Genghis Khan on his throne

GENGHIS KHAN
(circa 1162 – 1227)

The River Onon (on the borders between Mongolia and Siberia)
flowed peacefully in front of the camp. A procession of the most able
horsemen of the various tribes entered and then left the large tent in
the centre. It seemed that the entire population of the steppes had gathered together to honour
Temüjin, the commander who had united all the tribes of Mongolia, and after a series of successful
conquests, was now looking towards the whole of Asia Minor as his domain. When the procession
was over, a stake was driven into the hard, icy ground, bearing the flag of the Mongols, a white flag
with nine points. The great conqueror, now with the new title of 'Genghis Khan' (Lord of the
Ocean) then greeted his people, delighted by their cheers.

In 1206, most of the Asiatic population of the steppes (Merkits, Tartars and Kereit) gathered
together in the outskirts of the Borscovocny Mountains to proclaim as their chief the Mongol
Conqueror Temüjin (from then on called Genghis Khan), the only unbeatable warrior that they
had ever known. In Genghis Khan, the wish to conquer was closely linked with the desire to get
his revenge on those who had killed his father.

Temüjin (Genghis Khan) was born around 1162. His family were members of the Borjigin, a royal clan of Mongol warriors with a vast following of fine horsemen. At first, he was destined to follow in their footsteps. But after the death of his father, Yesügei, he and his family were captured by the Taychuit clan and made to live as slaves. None of this affected **Temüjin's** ability on horseback, nor his talents for seeing ways of defeating his enemies. Whilst still a slave, he escaped from the **Taitsiut**, whom he later defeated.

In 1184, with just a small army, plus the protection of a group of personal bodyguards **Temüjin** left for his first battle. This was against the Merkit tribe, who had earlier attacked his wife **Börte**. His victory was the first stage in a long war for the domination of the Orient, during which he would cross the whole of Asia, leaving behind him those who were either defeated, destitute or dead. **After the submission of the Tartars, the Kereit and the Naiman**, he began the invasion of China in 1211. This needed much more time and a greater commitment by his followers than previous conquests, but in 1214, the Chinese capital **Cambaluc** (later Beijing) was reduced to a mass of fire and rubble. After the conquest of China, Genghis Khan led his own army towards Persia to fight against the Kalif Mohammed entering the city of Samarkand in triumph in 1221. By this time, Genghis Khan and his troops were exhausted as a result of the long years in battle. And so he came to a stop in the Chinese region of of Gansu in 1227. A year before he died, he succeeded in carrying out one last undertaking – the defeat of the Tangut, the only people who, in 1210, had succeeded in beating him.

Photograph left, a Mongol encampment

Below, in square frame, Mongol horsemen

A princess with Genghis Khan

The Cruel Law-Maker

Genghis Khan made himself undisputed chief of the nomad population of Asia, by using systematic and tyrannical force. Born and brought up in the Asiatic steppes, an immense, barren and wild area, he had always been aware of the fights for power which were continually taking place within various Mongol tribes. At a very young age, he took part in the killing of the chief of a Tartar group, and when he was little more than fifteen years old, he had killed his stepbrother, Bekter, so that he could become chief of his own group.

When he became Genghis Khan (sovereign) of the Mongols, he realized that in order to ensure the stability of his kingdom, it was necessary to control and to discipline the behaviour of his subjects. From 1206, he introduced a series of laws for a strict community life (written down in the *Great Book of Jasaq*). Divorce was forbidden, the consumption of alcoholic drinks was limited and any sort of violence in sacred places was condemned.

Marco Polo

According to numerous legends, the figure of Genghis Khan was linked to the theme of light – born by a ray from the Sun and dying in a flash of lightning.

Death of Genghis Khan

In the presence of the Great Khan

The book *The Travels of Marco Polo* (originally known as *The Milione*) is the account in the form of a novel of a long journey to the Orient (from 1271 to 1295) undertaken by the Venetian explorer Marco Polo (1254-1324). Dictated to his close companion Rusticano of Pisa, when both were prisoners of the Genovese (around 1298), it tells of the incredible experiences seen at the court of Cathay (the ancient name for China). Marco Polo was guest of the Great Kublai Khan (1215-1294), grandson of Genghis Khan. He became sole emperor of the Mongols in 1260, and made Cambaluc (later Beijing) the capital of his kingdom. In 1279, he founded the Chinese dynasty Yuan. Unlike Genghis Khan, who had terrorized the Orient with his military campaigns, the Great Khan established a peaceful relationship with the Eastern governments, often welcoming foreign visitors (among them, Marco Polo).

Marco Polo before the Great Khan

The Origin of a Recipe

If on a restaurant menu you order 'steak tartare' you will be served with a plate of raw meat finely chopped, softened in wine or vinegar and seasoned with a little onion, capers and a sprinkling of pepper. This recipe comes from a food habit of the Tatars, re-named '**Tartars**' by the orientals because of their cruelty (in ancient language 'Tartara' meant 'hell'). This nomadic Asian population, defeated by Genghis Khan in the thirteenth century, spent long periods on horseback, moving continuously in search of food. To store the meat of animals which they caught from time to time, they adopted an ingenious (but unhygienic) method of placing the meat between the saddle and the horse so that, as the rider continually rubbed the saddle against the horse's back, the meat would become tender and fit to eat, even after some days.

In the painting to the left, Mongol horsemen

Below, slices of bread covered with 'steak tartare'

As well as 'steak tartare', there is also 'tartare sauce' (in photograph above) a thick liquid rather like a mayonnaise, made with egg yolks, chopped parsley and spices.

Mongol nomads cooking near their tents

The Lord of Florence who brought peace and harmony to politics and to art

LORENZO DE' MEDICI

(Florence 1449 – 1492)

The solemn voice of the priest resounded through the Church of Santa Maria del Fiore in Florence. The fine mist of incense rose into the air, creating a holy atmosphere to prepare for the most solemn moment of the Mass for Easter Sunday. Then, as the priest paused, there were shouts and cries, and a group of men burst out of their hiding places and ran into the central aisle, towards the de' Medici brothers, Guiliano and Lorenzo, as they knelt in prayer. Giuliano fell to the ground, fatally stabbed. Lorenzo was injured, but he rushed over to the body of their close friend Francesco Nori, who had died trying to help Guiliano. Meanwhile, the people were running in all directions, shouting and jostling each other as they tried to leave the church - whilst in front of the altar the pool of the victim's blood became larger and larger.

Medal commemorating Giuliano de' Medici

In 1478, some noble Florentine families, lead by the Pazzi bank, organized a plot to kill Giuliano and Lorenzo de' Medici, Lords of Florence. The two brothers had succeeded their father, **Piero de' Medici**, in 1469 as governors of the city. The aim of the plot was to bring Florence under the control of Rome. But Lorenzo survived and had the assassins of Guiliano executed almost immediately.

Pope Sixtus II had been involved in the Pazzi conspiracy, and he demanded that Lorenzo should be handed over to him. The Pope's plan was to help his supporter, the King of Naples, **Ferdinand I of Aragon**, to rule over Florence, so that he could still keep control. But, almost immediately after the assassination of Guiliano, the people of Florence made it clear that they wanted Lorenzo to govern them, rather than Pope Sixtus II and the King of Naples. In the end, Lorenzo decided to go to Naples to see the King, despite the fact that Ferdinand I of Aragon was known to be a cruel dictator. Lorenzo de' Medici reached the court of Ferdinand in 1480, and succeeded in persuading the king to allow him to remain as Lord of Florence. Without the support of Ferdinand, Pope Sixtus II was forced to accept the agreement between the two men.

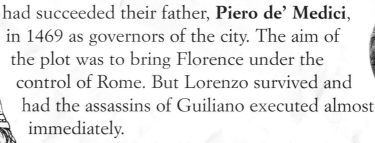

Ferdinand I of Aragon, King of Naples

The way in which he had faced up to both Pope Sixtus II and the powerful King of Naples made Lorenzo de' Medici very much respected among the people of Florence. They gave him the name of 'The Magnificent', meaning a truly great man. Leading members of the nobility also thought him very wise, calling him '**the needle on the Italian scales**', meaning that Lorenzo was the person who kept the kingdom steady and at peace. At that time, the whole of Italy was broken up into lots of little states, many of whom were not friendly towards each other. This made the country weak, so that it was constantly threatened by foreign rulers who wanted to expand their domains. Peace was finally established after the **Peace of Lodi** (1454) signed by dukes of Milan and the state of Venice, and the formation of the **Lega Italica (Italian League)** an agreement between different Italian kings. None of this would have taken place without Lorenzo de' Medici and the work which he did in breaking down hostilities between the Italian states. Many historians see his death in 1492 at only forty three years of age as the beginning of Italy's decline. Only two years later, the King of France, **Charles VIII**, entered Italy with his army – the first of a long list of sovereigns who would invade the country.

A villa at Careggi, where Lorenzo de' Medici died

Fascia of the church of Santa Maria Novella painted by Leon Battista Alberti

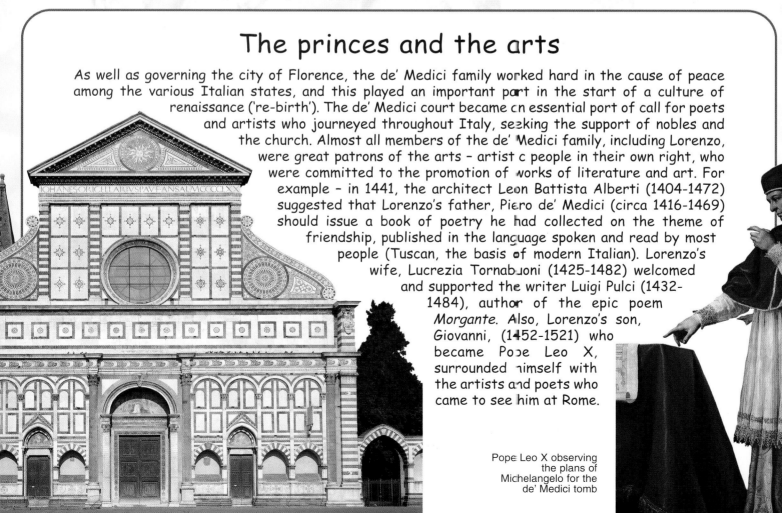

The princes and the arts

As well as governing the city of Florence, the de' Medici family worked hard in the cause of peace among the various Italian states, and this played an important part in the start of a culture of renaissance ('re-birth'). The de' Medici court became an essential port of call for poets and artists who journeyed throughout Italy, seeking the support of nobles and the church. Almost all members of the de' Medici family, including Lorenzo, were great patrons of the arts – artistic people in their own right, who were committed to the promotion of works of literature and art. For example – in 1441, the architect Leon Battista Alberti (1404-1472) suggested that Lorenzo's father, Piero de' Medici (circa 1416-1469) should issue a book of poetry he had collected on the theme of friendship, published in the language spoken and read by most people (Tuscan, the basis of modern Italian). Lorenzo's wife, Lucrezia Tornabuoni (1425-1482) welcomed and supported the writer Luigi Pulci (1432-1484), author of the epic poem *Morgante*. Also, Lorenzo's son, Giovanni, (1452-1521) who became Pope Leo X, surrounded himself with the artists and poets who came to see him at Rome.

Pope Leo X observing the plans of Michelangelo for the de' Medici tomb

63

The Emperor who reigned over a global kingdom on which the Sun never set

CHARLES V OF HABSBURG

(Gand 1500 – San Jerónimo de Yuste 1558)

A platoon of soldiers and horses and a handful of knights, armed only with axes mounted on poles, accompanied the carriage of the old sovereign. This was no armed guard led by an Emperor-Commander, but the court of a tired king, who had decided to leave the magnificence of his court to retire into a lonely Spanish monastery. As the warm mist veiled the ground and hid a path which was normally clear and sunny, so the happy memories of his youth seemed to vanish. As a boy, he had inherited the throne, crossing to Spain on horseback to take the royal crown. Now, before the eyes of King Charles V of Habsburg, there flowed visions of his past life, his domains, his lands and his people. Now had arrived the moment of rest and reflection, the time to understand that power can crumble like dust.

Abdication of Charles V

In 1556, the Emperor Charles V decided to abdicate, dividing his vast kingdom between his brother **Ferdinand I**, who also inherited the title of Emperor, and his son **Philip II**. The following year, he carried out the long journey across Spain to the monastery of Saint Jerónimo de Yuste where he decided to spend the rest of his life. He had been proclaimed King Charles V of Spain following the death of his mother's father, **Ferdinand II**, forty years before, in 1516, and had set foot on Spanish soil for the first time the following year. Born at Gand in the Netherlands in 1500, Charles had been made Duke of Bourbon in 1515. In 1519, on the death of the Emperor **Maximillian I of Habsburg** (his father's father) he also became the ruler of German domains, with the possibility of becoming Emperor.

Charles of Bourbon leading the lancers in the Sack of Rome

After a fierce electoral campaign against **Francis I**, the King of France, he was at last crowned Emperor of Austria in 1520.

During his long reign, Charles V experienced many difficulties, especially because his rival Francis I wanted to rule Italy. He also had to deal with the rebellion of German princes who had become Protestant followers of the reformer **Martin Luther**, plus the problem of Turkish pirates whose attacks were damaging trading ships in the Mediterranean Sea. Between military successes and victorious battles (for example, the conquest of Tunis, where the leader of the Turkish invaders, Khayr-al-Din called 'the **Barbarossa**', was defeated), Charles V was almost continually challenged by threats from dissatisfied followers, such as the revolt by German Protestant soldiers during the battle to occupy Italy – the same Germans who supported him when he decided to march against the Pope, plundering and looting Rome in the **Sack of Rome** (1527).

Armour of a German
Protestant soldier

Charles V on horseback, *by the Italian artist* **Tiziano Vecello** *(1490-1576). The picture was painted in 1548, one year after the imperial victory of Mühlberg against the Protestants.*

Joan of Castile,
portrait by Juan de Flandes

Madness?

The mother of Charles V, **Joan of Castile** (1479-1555) was called 'Joan the Mad'. From 1509, she was shut away in a castle in the city of Tordesillas. It has often been thought that this queen became 'mad' at the death of her husband, but this cannot be proved. The daughter of King Ferdinand III of Aragon and Isabel of Castile, it is known that Joan had suffered from depression even as a child, a state which seems to be present even in pictures of her. She fell in love with the husband that her parents had chosen for her, **Philip I of Habsburg**, called 'Philip I, the handsome', and was broken-hearted at his death as a young man in 1506. However, many people wondered if Joan's 'madness' was an excuse which was used by her father Ferdinand and afterwards, his son, Charles V, for keeping her in the castle.

Joan at the funeral of her husband, in a painting by Francisco Pradilla y Ortiz

The French king who believed that he was God's representative on Earth

LOUIS XIV
(San Germain-en-Laye 1638 – Versailles 1715)

The herald solemnly announced the beginning of the games, and people thronged excitedly around the space which had been cleared for the tournament. The fine silk dresses worn by the ladies added to the colourful spectacle. Soon, there was the first burst of applause and loud cheers as a knight spurred his horse into a gallop and threaded his lance through a ring, high up on a post. Suddenly, there was a fanfare of trumpets, and the spectators fell to their knees. As they knelt on the ground, a man glided past on his high-heeled shoes, nodding and smiling. It was King Louis XIV himself, the young sovereign whose handsome face crowned by long, dark brown hair, his strong, muscular body and complete air of royalty made him so admired by his people.

Cardinal Mazarin

In 1664, Louis XIV invited a large gathering of important French people to the opening of the **Palace of Versailles**. The palace was not yet complete – but the king needed to present the right image, so that everyone would know that France was to be governed by an all-powerful sovereign. Despite Louis XIV ascending to the French throne in 1643, when he was only five years old, it had been **Cardinal Jules Mazarin** who ruled the country until 1661. He had assumed this important position, after helping the mother of Louis XIV, **Anne of Austria**, when she was queen. Now, the Cardinal had died.

The first years of the reign of Louis XIV had been unsettled, with many rebellions between 1648 and 1653. First, there was a rebellion by the **Paris Parlement** (from the French verb 'parler', meaning 'to talk'), a powerful court of law who opposed Mazarin. This sparked off a long-running civil war, known as the **Fronde**, and which included another rebellion, this time by the

Louis XIV on horseback, statue by the sculptor Gian Lorenzo Bernini

nobility. The king was forced to flee and live in poverty, and it seemed that the monarchy would collapse. But Mazarin succeeded in overcoming all the rebels. After Mazarin's death, Louis XIV began strengthening his own power, seeking support from the middle classes to exercise more control over the nobility, most of whom he no longer trusted. He became known as 'the **Sun King**' – because, like the Sun around which the planets orbited, everything revolved around Louis XIV. After having overcome most of the unrest within France, the king turned his attention to French territories which were now controlled by foreign powers – the Frankish kingdom, for example (now northern France, Belgium and western Germany) was under the rule of Spain. The reign of Louis XIV was characterized by countless wars, the longest of which was over the succession of the Spanish throne. This war ended in 1714, with the throne of Spain passing to the grandson of Louis XIV, but at great cost to France. Louis XIV died the following year, 1715.

Portrait of Louis XIV

Lance made of steel, gold and wood, used by the soldiers in the bodyguard of Louis XIV

A woman at war

In July 1652, Paris was in turmoil. Many nobles had formed **the Princes' Fronde** and had captured the city. A cousin of the king, **Anne-Marie of Orléans** took command of a small group of supporters from Orléans, and then took possession of the Paris prison, the Bastille – just as the French peasants would do on 14 July 1789 when the French Revolution began. She fired the cannon of the Bastille against the troops of Louis XIV. As a result, she was banished into exile in 1652 when the king returned to Paris, until 1657, when she was released because Louis XIV wanted her to marry King Alfonso VI of Portugal. Once again, Anne-Marie defied the king, and was sent into exile again until 1664 when she was allowed to marry of her own free will.

A dream of a palace

Versailles was not just a palace, but a little city, with buildings, streets, streams and gardens. This complex monument was built by Louis XIV as a home for his own family, with grounds in which to grow food for his many servants and guards, and enough space to welcome vast numbers of important guests. As well as a place of relaxation, Versailles also gave Louis XIV more control over his life. After the rebellions in the first years of his reign, the king did not trust many of the French nobility and preferred to have them at Paris. Versailles had originally been a hunting lodge, but the king did not take heed of the enormous costs of restoring and enlarging the royal estate. He was only interested in immortalizing his name in marble sculptures, in frescos, in statues and in fountains, taking all he wanted from the money reserves of France. When the French court transferred permanently to Versailles in 1682, the European rulers who visited saw the palace as the sort of home they wanted to have. And so the **Palace of Caserta** (Italy), the **Schönbrunn** (Vienna) and the **Castle of Potsdam** (near Berlin) were all built.

Versailles in a painting by Patel

The general who claimed the title of Emperor in battle

NAPOLEON BONAPARTE

(Ajaccio, Corsica 1769 – Saint Helena 1821)

Darkness fell slowly across the battlefield. From the ground there rose up the cries of pain from the wounded and the wheezes of horses in agony. The battlefield of Waterloo was an expanse of bodies, the soldiers who had not been seriously injured wandered around among the bodies like ghosts. Their General, Napoleon Bonaparte, had already fled from the horror, but they did not know this. What were now dead bodies had been men marching off to war in glory and who had now met their end. Where was their Emperor, their commander who had led them in triumph, once seeming all-conquering and unbeatable? They just could not believe or understand what had happened…

The **Battle of Waterloo** on 18 July 1815 was seen as the end of the long history of Napoleon Bonaparte. Defeated by a combined force of Austrians, Germans and British, the French Emperor fled from the scene of battle. He was exiled to the island of Saint Helena, where he died in 1821. His incredible rise to power began in Ajaccio, Corsica, where Napoleon Bonaparte was born in 1769 into a noble but poor family. He was sent to school in Paris, and when he left in 1790, he became actively involved in the French Revolution. He joined the French army and soon proved to be so outstanding in military tactics, that he was made an Officer and rose to the position of General. In 1796, he was put in charge of a campaign in Italy against the Austrians. Two years later, he

The flight of Napoleon from the battlefield of Waterloo

commanded the French armies fighting the Turkish troops in Egypt. All this led the way to power, followed by organizing a **Coup d'État** (overthrow of government) on 9 November 1799. A few years afterwards, in 1804, he would achieve the highest honour. On 2 December he was crowned Emperor at the cathedral of Notre Dame in Paris. His first task was to establish his own government as he wanted, by a series of laws and a new Civil Code issued in 1804 (the **Code Napoléon**). At the same time, he continued his policy of conquests, especially against the Austrians and the British. The victories of **Austerlitz, Jena** and **Friedland** (1806) and later of **Wagram** (1809) made many people believe that he would dominate the whole of Europe. The disastrous ending of the **war against Russia** in 1812 began to break down the myth that he was unbeatable. After Napoleon was defeated by the Austrians at Arcis-sur-Aube in1814, he was exiled to the Isle of Elba. After one hundred days, he escaped and returned to France, ready to plan what was to be his final battle at Waterloo. Exiled once again, he died on the island of Saint Helena in 1821.

In a letter sent to Pope Pius VII, Napoleon wrote 'I am Charlemagne', claiming to be the new Holy Roman Emperor.

Statue of Paolina Borghese, sister of Napoleon, by Antonio Canova

Napoleon during the Russian campaign by E. Meissonier

The most bitter of battles

Even the greatest Generals make mistakes - or perhaps it is just a matter of luck. Yet throughout history, whole countries have suffered shortages and starvation due to errors made by military commanders. Napoleon's huge mistake was when he thought he would be able to conquer Russia. The army which he commanded was powerless on the Russian battlefield. The French had to move away rapidly from enemy territory in order to reinforce their troops – but they did not take into account that the Russians would withdraw further inwards, burning everything as they went. At last, with the onset of winter, Napoleon was forced to order the withdrawal of his troops. During the long march home, many of his men died from cold and from hunger.

Yet, despite the experience of Napoleon, Adolf Hitler also ordered a campaign against Russia during the Second World War. But, as with Napoleon, he also undervalued the bravery of the Russians, the enormous areas which had to be covered and, most of all, the bitterness of the climate.

German troops in Russia during the Second World War

The boy Pharaoh who achieved fame by death

TUTANKHAMUN

(circa 1370 BC – circa 1352 BC)

Even after the discovery of the tomb and the numerous examinations carried out on his mummified body, little is known about Tutankhamun. When he became pharaoh at the age of about nine years old, Egypt was troubled by religious conflicts within the country. The pharaoh, **Amenhotep IV** (re-named Akhenaton), Tutankhamun's predecessor, had abolished the many Egyptian gods to strengthen the following of just one god, Aton. Officials and priests ruled the country in the first years of Tutankhamun's reign because he was too young to govern alone and they re-established old traditions.

To begin with, the real name of the boy pharaoh was actually Tutankhaton, but this was changed to Tutankhamun as a sign of the return to old titles and customs. The reign of Tutankhamun was too short to allow any great achievements – he died at about eighteen years of age. His **tomb** was modest compared to other pharaohs and without any of the usual funeral furnishings, suggesting that he died suddenly. Many theories have been put forward as to the cause of his death – a health problem present from birth, an infectious illness, an accident, a murder ... Many of these theories have been

A fresco painting in the buried chamber of Tutankhamun

investigated, and an autopsy has been carried out by expert **pathologists**. They found breaks in the bones of the skull, but it was impossible to say if these had happened before or after death. And so the doubt remains as to whether he fell from his chariot on which he loved to go hunting, or if he became ill as the result of an insect bite, or if someone killed him in a court conspiracy.

The sixth sense of an explorer

Howard Carter (1873-1939) arrived in Egypt at the end of the 19th century as a talented artist. The Egypt Exploration Fund, set up by the British for students of archaeology, needed someone who could reproduce the pictures on the walls of Egyptian tombs on to paper and Carter was well suited for the job. But being in the land of the pharaohs made the young artist determined to investigate the mysteries of these ancient rulers, as well as copying the pictures that they had left behind. Convinced that he was on the track of the burial chambers of the legendary Egyptian king Tutankhamun, Carter persuaded Lord Carnarvon (1866-1923) to finance a proper archaeological expedition. In 1922, when he had almost given up, Carter found Tutankhamun's tomb, hidden under ancient huts of workmen. Then came a further sensational discovery. By some miracle, the tomb had not been plundered and still contained all the treasures of the pharaoh (over five thousand fine objects), that included furnishings, clothes and wonderful jewels.

Excavations in the tomb of a Pharaoh

PRINCESSES
QUEENS
and
EMPRESSES

The woman who reigned over Egypt with the male title of Pharaoh

HATSHEPSUT
(circa late 16th Century – circa 1482 BC)

The first rays of dawn filtered through into the room of Hatshepsut. She lay back, thinking hard. At the end of a long, sleepless night, she had made a decision, and in a short time she would put her ideas into action. There was a knock at the door. Then came the voice of her faithful steward, Senenmut. The moment had arrived. Soon the Egyptian people would no longer have a princess regent, nor even a young queen, but a proper pharaoh who could rule completely. Hatshepsut rose slowly and went to the room of her dead husband, Thutmosis II. After taking from a casket the crown jewels (the crown of Upper and Lower Egypt, the sceptre and the false beard, traditionally worn only by the king) she dressed in men's clothes and left her apartments. Now she was the daughter of Amon-Ra, Egyptian god of the Sun, and the new pharaoh.

From about 1479 BC, Hatshepsut was the wife of the Egyptian sovereign **Thutmosis II**, her half-brother (both were children of **Thutmosis I**). As the daughter and the wife of a pharaoh, she was an important person, but always remained in second place to her husband, as a woman was then expected to do. On the death of her husband, she was faced with the prospect of ruling Egypt in the place of the young successor, her nephew and stepson, Thutmosis III. For some years, she had taken her place as Regent to the pharaoh, but then she decided (we do not know quite when) to assume the title of Pharaoh – even though she was a woman, something unheard of in the history of ancient Egypt.

From that moment she dressed in a man's clothes, with the traditional false beard of Egyptian sovereigns, looking exactly the same as a man. Surrounded by her faithful staff, such as **Senenmut**, she established a political system based on trade between Egypt and other countries. During her reign there were no wars. Instead, Hatshepsut opened up routes towards the African markets such as the **kingdom of Punt**. Hatshepsut's fleets sailed from Egypt with weapons and jewels and returned loaded with ivory, ebony, plants and animals. At Hatshepsut's death, which is believed to have been in 1458 BC, Thutmosis III, the rightful pharaoh and exiled from the throne, rose to power again; but Egypt had lost a great and a charming pharaoh – a woman.

Hatshepsut with the god *Amon-Ra*

Massacre in the shadow of the temple

The temple of Djeser-djeseru, 'sacred of sacreds', was built on the orders of Hatshepsut, sheltered by a jutting-out rock in the area known today as Deir-El-Bahari ('Monastery of the North' because there is now a monastery there). The temple, built under the close supervision of Senenmut is made up of a series of chapels and rooms, at three different levels. Between the floors, connected by ramps, were long, richly decorated colonnades. The temple has become the destination of tourists and was the scene in 1997 of a bloody act of terrorism. An armed group, apparently from the Islamic organization Jamaa Islamya, opened fire on a group of Swiss, Germans, English and Japanese tourists, killing 67 people.

The temple of Hatshepsut

Desecration and an insult

Thutmosis III, crowned alongside his aunt and stepmother Hatshepsut, had to live for over twenty years as an outcast. So it would have been easy to assume that on the death of Hatshepsut he might do everything he could to destroy her memory. But he did not. When he became Pharaoh of Egypt, he devoted much of his reign to widening the borders of Egypt out towards Asia. But in the last years of his life, the memory of Hatshepsut returned to dominate his thoughts most powerfully. Perhaps on the advice of some members of the priesthood, Thutmosis III undertook a campaign for the destruction (fortunately only partial) of the statues and images of the woman pharaoh. This was not only an act of desecration, but also a most serious insult, because statues and images were seen by the ancient Egyptians as a method by which a dead person could enter the after-life.

FASCINATING FACT
The track from the Valley of Kings (where the tombs of the pharaohs were found) leading to the temple of Hatshepsut, is called 'Agatha Christie Path' in honour of the author who described it in her book 'Death Comes as the End' written in 1945.

Poster advertising the film
Death on the Nile

*The highest part of this column is called the **hathorica** because it was built in the temple dedicated to the god Hathor. It is shaped like a musical instrument, the sithar.*

A fabulous land

The reign of Hatshepsut was marked by prosperity and peace. Excluding small skirmishes with the Nubian people (short-lived battles in which most probably even the pharaoh took part) there was no need for an army to keep the peace. Instead, there were expeditions, such as the exploration along the coast of the Red Sea, towards the mythical **people of Punt**. The account of this voyage, carved into the sandstone walls of the temple of Hatshepsut, describes exotic animals and plants which has helped studies of locations in the land of Punt, today known as the Horn of Africa, (Somalia, Eritrea).

Tributes to Egypt sent by the people of Punt

*The queen who transformed England
into a powerful sea-going nation*

QUEEN ELIZABETH I
(Greenwich 1533 – Richmond 1603)

*The landscape of the gardens at Hatfield Palace in Hertfordshire
restored Elizabeth's young spirit. After having been imprisoned in
the Bell Tower at the Tower of London, she did not mind the
solitude of Hatfield where it was all so beautifully peaceful. Yet, as
long as her half-sister Mary was alive, there could be no peace for
Elizabeth, Mary's heir. The queen might be dying, but Elizabeth was
suffering, too. At court, she was unpopular, mistrusted and regarded
with suspicion and unwillingly drawn into the intrigues of the palace,
no matter how much she tried to avoid this. The continuing anxiety was
exhausting even for Elizabeth's strong character. She hardly noticed a
messenger advancing silently, until he bowed and held out a ring on a cushion. This meant that
Mary was dead. Now it was Elizabeth's task to reign over the kingdom of England.*

On 17 November 1558, Elizabeth I ascended to the English throne, on the death of her half-sister
Mary Tudor. The country over which she was to reign, England, was torn apart as the result of
battles between Catholics and Protestants. The rule of the Catholic Mary (called 'Bloody Mary'
because of her killing of Protestants) had created deep divisions between people of different
religions. Having grown up among plotters and assassins, including those who had plotted against
her mother, **Anne Boleyn**, Elizabeth had learned from a child how to deal with the hidden
dangers of power and government. The methods which she had learned were not all that
different from those of Mary, but Elizabeth also had a natural ability to deal with people and for
getting her own way. Using these skills, Elizabeth succeeded in obtaining something which none
of her predecessors, not even her father **Henry VIII**, had succeeded in achieving – the unity, and
consequently, the development of England. After reaffirming in 1559 the **Act of Supremacy** (set
down in 1534 by her father), her **Act of Uniformity** and the Book of Common Prayer firmly
established the protestant Church of England. Her reign was marked by a rebirth of the arts and

Fleet of the British East India Company

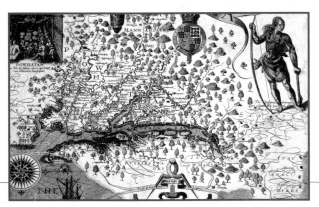

Map of Virginia, discovered by Walter Raleigh

commerce. Surrounded by writers, and a lover of ballet and music, Elizabeth was basically a down-to-earth woman. Secretly, she supported the **privateers**, (men in her service who attacked and robbed foreign ships, especially those of the Spanish Armada), giving a boost to her merchant ships. Following the victory by her ships over those of the Spanish king **Philip II** in the English Channel (1588), England became the true 'ruler of the waves'. Elizabeth ruled alone and never married. So, at her death in 1603, her nephew **King James I of Scotland**, and son of Mary Stuart (**Mary Queen of Scots**), the cousin Elizabeth had had assassinated, inherited the English crown.

Six wives for one king

Henry VIII, father of Elizabeth, founded the Church of England so that he could divorce his first wife. In reality, his motives were mainly political and economic; by establishing the Church of England, he could reign without any interference by the Pope; and, by abolishing the Catholic clergy, he could claim their grounds and their enormous wealth. But this was also the start of a married life which was constantly changing.

Catherine of Aragon: Henry's first wife. After her divorce she died in almost complete solitude. Her daughter was Mary I.

Anne Boleyn: the lady in waiting for whom Henry divorced Catherine. She was accused of adultery and beheaded. She was the mother of Elizabeth I.

Jane Seymour: she lived only a few days after giving birth to Henry's only male heir, Edward VII.

Anne of Cleves: she was divorced soon after the wedding.

Catherine Howard: cousin of Anne Boleyn; she was also beheaded.

Catherine Parr: the only one of Henry's queens who survived him.

Clockwise from top: Catherine Parr, Jane Seymour, Anne Boleyn, the family of Henry VIII, Catherine of Aragon, Henry VIII.

Mary Queen of Scots

The tragic life of Mary Stuart

On 1 February 1587, Elizabeth gave orders for the execution of her cousin **Mary Stuart** (Mary, Queen of Scots), who had been accused of treason. The execution, which took place a few days later, was very brutal. It took three blows of the axe to behead Mary and when it seemed that there was no life in her dead body, the executioner saw that she was still moving. In fact, it was a dog who had crawled in among her clothes. And so Mary's life ended as the scene from a horror film. In contrast, part of her earlier life was a story of love (with marriage and jealousy), then a horror story (with plotters and assassins) and a detective story (with imprisonment and intrigues). Immortalized by numerous writers such as **Vittorio Alfieri** (1749–1803) and **Friedrich Schiller** (1759–1805), she still lives in all her tragic grandeur in their plays.

An 'almost' invincible armada

Philip II had many reasons for hating Elizabeth – religion, power, but especially honour. Some years before, the English queen had refused his proposal of marriage. He decided to teach her a lesson in 1588, by forming a fleet which he called 'the **Invincible** (unbeatable) **Armada**, with the aim of invading England. In fact, the strong but hard-to-manage Spanish ships faced three enemies – hunger, the English ships and the many storms which sprung up in the English Channel. One by one, Philip's ships returned to Spain – not so invincible as he had claimed!

Battle between the English ships and the *Invincible Armada*

Sir Walter Raleigh (*circa 1522–1618*) *explored the coast of North America and established the English colony of Virginia, named in honour of Elizabeth 'the virgin queen'.*

The adventurer **Francis Drake** (*1539–1596*). *In 1577 he sailed from England with the Queen's blessing and money from the English crown. After three years of robbing and damage to the Spanish Armada, he returned to England with some splendid loot and was knighted 'Sir'.*

Bestseller at the English Court

Arts and learning flourished in the Elizabethan age. Philosophers (great thinkers) such as Francis Bacon, poets (Philip Sidney, Edmund Spenser, John Donne) and playwrights (William Shakespeare, Ben Jonson, Christopher Marlowe) raised England to the height of European culture. The plays and works of Shakespeare in particular became popular in almost every country. Four centuries have passed since Shakespeare's time. His work has been translated into all languages and he remains one of the best-selling writers in the world today.

Francis Bacon

Coin with the image of Elizabeth II

*E izabeth I, dressed in silver military armour, visits her troops at **Tilbury** before they set sail for battle against the fleet of Philip II of Spain*

Banquets in the open air

Elizabeth often had to receive a number of important guests for which there was not a large enough room. So, some gatherings were organized in the so-called '**open houses**' – huge structures set up in royal parks and which were removed as soon as the reception was over. These 'open houses' were made of cloths painted with country landscapes and held up by poles. Inside they were lit with spheres of glass carefully placed to create orbs of light and a fairytale atmosphere.

Queen Elizabeth I carried in court

The Tsarina who governed with a fist of steel and invited poets and writers to her court.

CATHERINE THE GREAT OF RUSSIA

Stettin, Prussia (now Szczecin) Poland 1729 – Tsarskoye Selo (now Pushkin) near St. Petersburg, Russia 1796

The carriage rolled rhythmically along the silent streets of Saint Petersburg, still lit by the pale light of the dawn. The lady in the carriage was feeling rather nervous. On the one hand, she wished she could lead the soldiers to proclaim her own triumph. On the other, she wanted to stop the horses, to slow them down so that her journey would last for ever. All at once, the coachman stopped the carriage in front of the barracks of the Izmajlovskij Regiment and helped her to descend. Immediately there came a cry of joy, as the crowd greeted their new Tsarina, a woman simply dressed and her hair ruffled. After her priest had raised a crucifix in blessing, Catherine went back into the carriage, thinking of all the others who had tried to claim the throne of Russia.

On 28 June 1762, Catherine, wife of Tsar Peter III, carried out a **coup d'état** (overthrow of government) with the help of an army. Her husband, penniless and imprisoned, died, probably murdered, a few days after. From then on, for over thirty years, 'Catherine the Great' would reign over Russia. Born Sofia di Anhalt-Zerbst, she was the daughter of a German prince. Nobody could have predicted that she would achieve such fame and power.

Coronation of Catherine the Great

She arrived in Russia in 1745 to marry the heir to the throne and was officially declared Tsarina on 22 September 1762. From then on, Catherine had to fight hard to overcome all the suspicion and plotting at the court of the Tsar. Intelligent and a lover of culture, she was dominated by her husband, a mean man, a heavy drinker and influenced by the mood swings of his aunt, the Empress Elizabeth. Almost as soon as he became Tsar, **Peter III** promised to give the Russian people a **legislative code** to establish true justice. In this, Peter was inspired by the theories laid down by European thinkers written in a document called the **Nakaz** and which would provide the basis for the discussions of the Russian law-making assembly. But this folded in 1768 without having changed any of the existing legal system.

Catherine did not obtain great results in such internal politics, but she did achieve incredible military success. Under her rule, the Turkish armies were defeated in the first **Russian Turkish War** (1768–1774) followed by success against the Ottoman Empire between 1787 and 1792. During her reign, after the collapse of the Polish monarchy, Russia gained vast areas of land to the east from Poland.

Catherine's Palace at Saint Petersburg

Powerful women

Before the reforms of Tsar Peter I 'the Great', the Russian female nobility was only allowed to support their husbands and bring up their families. So it is still astounding that, from 1725–1796, Russia was ruled by four women. The tsarinas who succeeded to the throne, **Catherine I**, Anna Ivanovna, Elizaveta Petrovna and Catherine II ('The Great') all had considerable charm, intelligence and were full of life. They were also ruthless in getting their own way. Each of them continued the work of Tsar **Peter I** to make Russia culturally superior to Europe by inviting clever and famous Europeans to their courts and patronizing the arts and sciences. The four tsarinas also equalled the male tsars in cruelty. Anna and Elizaveta, for example, had special rooms for mentally-ill and deformed people to provide entertainment and played little 'jokes' at their expense.

Catherine with Tsar Peter I 'The Great'

Tsarina Catherine I

An 'enlightened' sovereign

Catherine was a real friend of philosophers, the great thinkers. The Tsarina had a deep regard for the most famous and most intelligent of scholars, especially the French. Many times, she tried to persuade those who admired her most to make the long journey to her court. Some, such as the Italian **Cesare Beccaria** (1738–1794), author of the book *On Crimes and Punishments* (1880), and a great admirer of the Russian sovereign, declined the invitation. Others, like Voltaire (1694–1778) preferred a relationship at a distance, exchanging letters on art and politics with the Tsarina. However, the writers **Denis Diderot** (1713–1784) and **Jean Le Rond d'Alembert** (1717–1783) who worked together to undertake the French translation of the famous Chambers Encyclopaedia, decided to journey to Saint Petersburg, where they stayed from the winter of 1773 to the Spring of 1774.

Denis Diderot, painting by Louis Michel Van Loo

Bloodshed leading to a new ruler

Catherine was accused, probably without cause, of being involved in the **murder** of her husband and the legitimate heir to the throne, **Peter III**, on 6 July 1762. After the coup d'état, her position as ruler was sometimes in danger. Some of the people were still faithful to Peter III, and many saw this as a reason to rise up against her. As long as Peter remained alive, Catherine's power was at risk. So, the news of her husband's death came as a relief for her. A guard was accused of the murder, but the assassination is believed to have been carried out by the family of Catherine's lover, Aleksey Grigoryevich Orlov, all of whom had much to gain from her accession to the throne.

Tsar Peter III

Cup with the Romanov coat of arms made for the wedding of Catherine II

The slaves of Catherine II

All the Russian rulers were faced with the problem of slavery. In fact, excluding only the families of the nobility, the members of the Russian Orthodox clergy, soldiers and a few peasants who were free, the major part of the Russian population consisted of the so-called 'servants' of the nobles – slaves tied to the land and to their often violent masters. Once Catherine came to power, she promised to improve the living conditions of the peasants; but despite her good intentions, her project for reform failed miserably. After the revolution which broke out in Russia between 1773 and 1774, the tsarina became even more obsessed with her position, concentrating more on maintaining her own power than the sad fate of her people in slavery.

*The Cossack **Yemelyan Pugachov** was a supporter of the exiled Tsar Peter III. In 1773, Pugachov's people were starving, due to the lack of concern of Catherine. So, he led the peasants in an uprising against her. For this, he was arrested by the Russian Army and imprisoned from 1774 until 1775 when he was publicly executed in Moscow.*

The soul of Russia

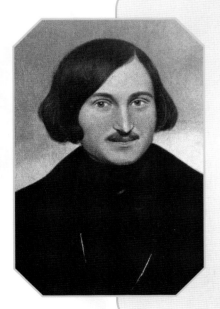

The Russian peasants were seen as 'souls' owned by their cruel masters in death as well as in life. Their sad fate and cruel living conditions were portrayed by the Russian writer **Nikolay Gogol** (1809–1852) in his novel *Dead Souls* published in 1842. Almost fifty years after the death of Catherine, the poor lives of the peasants, slaves of the Church, the crown and the nobility, had not changed.

Then came the denunciation of Gogol. Through the eyes of the criminal and cheat, Pavel Cicikov, the main character in his book, Cicikov's search for 'souls' would lead him into a despairing society, the people no longer even able to scream as they suffered.

After his dramatic novel *Lost Souls* Nikolay Gogol wrote other theatrical works and numerous accounts based on Russian traditions and legends.

It is believed by some that **Anastasia**, youngest daughter of Tsar Nicolas II, survived the execution of the Romanov family at Ekaterinburg during the Russian Revolution in 1919. If this were true, then she would have been the heiress to the royal house of Imperial Russia.

The empress who fought to be recognized as the rightful heir to the throne

MARIA THERESA OF AUSTRIA

(Vienna 1717 – 1780)

A young woman, attractive and elegant despite her plain black dress, walked determinedly through the huge room. Arriving in front of the throne, where her ancestors, the Habsburg sovereigns, had sat, she could not help thinking of the recent death of her father, the Emperor Charles VI. Her eyes filled with tears. But then her expression changed into one of determination. The Austrian kingdom was facing dangers which were too great to waste time on tears. Now, she was not only a daughter, a wife and a mother, but also Queen Maria Theresa, whose task it was to repel the attacks by foreign enemies. The first thing she did was to order the waiting court to come together before her. Then, the nobles of the kingdom officially paid homage to their new queen, kneeling at her feet.

At the end of October 1740, the Austrian sovereign, **Charles VI** died, leaving the Habsburg kingdom (Austria, Hungary, Bohemia and the dukedom of Milan) to his daughter Maria Theresa. This accession was made possible by a document, the **Pragmatic Sanction**, set down by the Emperor in 1713, which granted women accession to the throne of the royal house of Hapsburg. But some European sovereigns contested this succession and this resulted in a long war, later called the '**War of Austrian Succession**' (1740–1748). The first years of Maria Theresa's reign were clouded by continual conflicts, which seriously threatened her kingdoms. Although Maria Theresa had grown up without having been prepared for command of a kingdom, her natural common sense enabled her to limit the damage done through her inefficient generals, and show more ability than her husband, Francis Stephen of Lorraine (whom she married in 1736) in the management of the army. At the end of the war, with the **Treaty of Aix-la-Chapelle** (1748) Austria had to agree to the region of Silesia in Prussia, an area rich in mineral deposits, becoming part of the Prussian kingdom. After that, Queen Maria Theresa, who had already carried out many changes within her own country, now began to work on a series of reforms in the organization and the government of Austria, as well as changes in finance, in education and her military forces.

Thanks to her able system of government, the Hapsburg kingdom flourished again both in trade and in culture. In

Francis Stephen of Lorraine, husband of Maria Theresa

1756, together with the French monarchy, Austria again faced up to the Prussian Emperor Frederick II, with the aim of winning back the region of Silesia (**the Seven Years War**). Once again this led to harsh defeat. From 1765, the Queen, whom the Austrian people had learned to respect and to love as a stern but just mother, ruled together with her son Joseph II. On the death of Maria Theresa, he succeeded her in 1780.

The island of Minorca occupied by the English during the Seven Years War

The French Queen Marie Antoinette

Marie Antoinette is led to the scaffold

The tragic fate of a daughter

Marie Antoinette (1755–1793) was the second youngest of the sixteen daughters of Maria Theresa. When she arrived n France for the first time in 1770, she was the young wife of the heir to the French throne, the future **Louis XVI** (1754-1793). Then her arrival had been warmly celebrated by the French people. But within a few years, the feelings of the people for the fascinating princess had changed dramatically. Scornfully, they nicknamed her 'the Austrian' and she was criticized for her extravagance, her expensive tastes and her lack of commitment to France. Gradually, these bad feelings developed into signs of revolt, ending in the outbreak of the French Revolution (1789) Four years later, in 1793, Marie Antoinette and Louis XVI were condemned to death at the guillotine.

Maria Theresa's son, Peter Leopold Grand Duke of Tuscany, eliminated completely from his kingdom the use of torture and the death penalty (1786). In 1790, at the death of his brother Joseph II he obtained the title of Leopold II, Emperor.

The family of Peter Leopold of Tuscany

The queen who transformed the United Kingdom into a world power

QUEEN VICTORIA

(London 1819 – Osborne, Isle of Wight 1901)

Victoria wished she could sleep. King William IV was dead. It was only a matter of days, perhaps hours, and she would accede to the British throne. She knew that she was not prepared for this – but the thoughts which filled her mind were of the freedom which she would now experience, instead of being controlled by her powerful mother. She could not help being excited at the prospect. As the door to her chambers opened, she knew her sad and lonely childhood and her seclusion at Kensington Palace were well and truly over. Now she was Queen of the United Kingdom of Great Britain and Ireland. Rising from her bed, her young face was serious and mature, the look of a true monarch. When she had dressed, she received a visit from the Lord Chamberlain and then the Archbishop of Canterbury, who gave her the official news that she was now the new ruler.

On 20 June 1837, a little more than a month after her eighteenth birthday, Victoria of Hanover became Queen of the United Kingdom. Until then, she had lived at Kensington Palace, almost completely alone and without seeing any visitors. She seldom had contact with the royal court, held back by the ambition of her mother, also the distrust of the king **William IV**. At the death of the king, Victoria was completely free of her mother's guardianship, so that she could rule independently, and live at Buckingham Palace. Although she was not yet crowned Queen (her coronation would take place at Westminster Abbey on 28 June 1838), she had to face a difficult time because of the internal politics of her own country. The growing dissatisfaction of the lower classes led to the birth of **Chartism**, a working-class movement for the reform of parliament in 1837. By sending petitions to members of parliament and gaining support from the public, a series of social reforms were requested, including the right of all men to vote by ballot and the establishment of local councils. All of these Victoria's parliament rejected and when the movement's leaders protested, they were treated like convicts and banished to Australia. In addition, there was much discontent due to the high prices of corn, which many saw as the fault of the Corn Laws instituted by parliament.

The coronation of Queen Victoria

84

The first ten years of Victoria's reign were therefore troubled by the growing discontent of her people, continuing parliamentary crises and the news of unrest among the people of many European countries such as Italy and France. Many members of the British political classes, as well as Queen Victoria, feared that the revolts against the monarchies in European countries could also happen in the United Kingdom. During this time, Victoria found true

Funeral cortege of Victoria

Albert of Saxe Coburg-Gotha, husband of Victoria

consolation in her even-tempered husband **Albert of Saxe Coburg-Gotha** whom she married on 10 February 1840. Thanks to him, London successfully staged the first **International Exhibition** in 1851 – the same year in which it was seen that the dangers threatening the British crown seemed to have been avoided, also thanks to the influence of the wise Albert. But Victoria was not to have her beloved consort for ever. He died prematurely in 1861, on the eve of the South Kensington Exhibition in London, which he had also organized. But Victoria still held on to the determination which she had had since childhood. As well as having a large

family (nine children and numerous grand-children), she led her people towards the new twentieth century. Although during her reign there was much inequality and unfairness (such as the growing industrialization at the expense of the deterioration of living conditions of the workers), at her death Britain was a prosperous nation, leading the world in technology and with many **rich colonies** in Africa and in Asia (in 1876 Victoria had assumed the title of Empress of India). With the death of Queen Victoria a century of economic, political and social transformation closed, giving way to modern-day living.

Coal-mining in England

The advent of industrialization dramatically changed the urban landscape of the cities, such as Leigh in Scotland

In Africa in the name of Victoria

Lake Victoria, a huge lake surrounded by three African countries, Uganda, Kenya and Tanzania, and the **Victoria Falls** on the Zambezi River, are recorded in the journeys through Africa of fascinating but rather mysterious person – the Scottish missionary **David Livingstone** (1813–1873).

Arriving in Africa to carry out missionary works and to help the local people, Livingstone also became an explorer. Searching for the source of the River Nile, he entered into the heart of the African continent, where he made some of the most astounding discoveries, all of which he dedicated to Queen Victoria. But during his last African pilgrimage he vanished and it was the explorer **Henry Stanley** who was sent from England to find him. When, visiting a village, he saw a white man among members of an African tribe, it is said that Stanley announced, *'Doctor Livingstone, I presume'*. Who else could it be?

From top: dawn on Lake Victoria in Tanzania:
the Victoria Falls:
rafting among the rapids of the Zambezi River

The celebrated meeting of the missionary David Livingstone and the explorer Henry Stanley

A door towards the East ...

Among the works carried out during the reign of Queen Victoria, the construction of the **Suez Canal** was perhaps the most important. The whole project was completed in only eleven years, ending in 1869. Many nations as well as Great Britain had joined the French-owned **Suez Canal Company** which was founded with the aim of raising enough money for the monumental undertaking: 161 kilometres were excavated from rock to connect the Mediterranean in the West to the Red Sea in the East. In 1875, a few years after the work was finished, the British crown obtained the largest shareholding in the Company, thus guaranteeing its supremacy in trade with countries such as Australia and New Zealand, India and China.

THE SUEZ CANAL IS NATIONALIZED
In 1956, the Egyptian President, **Gamal Abdel Nasser** *(see photo right, Nasser being carried aloft in triumph) declared the nationalization of the Suez Canal: Great Britain, France and Israel, whose interests in the Canal were based on both trade and military position, sent their armed forces to stop him. At the end of the conflict, the United Nations Organization (UNO) entrusted the management of the canal to Egypt.*

The Suez Canal in a painting by Rieger

The Suez Canal, seen by satellite

An ancient idea ...

The idea of connecting the Mediterranean with the Red Sea was not first suggested during the reign of Victoria. In the seventh century BC, the Pharaoh **Necho II** decided to begin constructing a canal, which was finished around 490 BC by the Persian **Emperor Darius I**. He called it the 'Canal of the Pharaohs' and the aim was for the canal to provide a passage between the Nile delta and the Red Sea. This immense undertaking was defeated by nature; with the passage of time, the canal closed up again, clogged up by sand. Centuries later, a project to excavate a large strip of land between the Arab Desert and the Sinai peninsular was then put forward by the French Emperor **Napoleon Bonaparte**, but he did not have time to complete the work.

Napoleon in Egypt, painted by Henry Levy

A LIFE CUT SHORT

The Indian princess who became a Lady

POCAHONTAS

(circa 1595 – 1617)

During her short life (she was only twenty two years old when she died) Pocahontas underwent an astounding transformation from a 'redskin' princess of the great **Powhatan** (chief of the Potomac tribe) to a much-admired lady at the court of **King James I**.

In 1608, when she saved the life of captain **John Smith**, she was a young girl who had grown up in the forest (the lands of North America which Sir Walter Raleigh had named 'Virginia'). She knew little of the so-called 'white people' but, fascinated by Smith's blue eyes and blonde hair, she decided to oppose her father, who had condemned the adventurer to death.

For a time Pocahontas was also a prisoner in the English colonies, until she returned to her own people. Converted to Christianity and baptized '**Rebecca**', she married a farmer, **John Rolfe**. Received with honour by the English sovereign as an example of the possible integration between the old and the new world, she died of tuberculosis without ever returning to her own people again.

The young Pocahontas dressed in English costume

Fascinating facts

John Smith told of his meeting with the tribe of Powhatan in the book *The Generall Histories of Virginia of New England and the Summer Isles* (1624).

Pocahontas had wanted to work in a circus as an **acrobat**. During her visit to the fortress at Jamestown she stupefied the colonials by a display of her ability, during which she walked on her hands.

When, after she became Lady Rebecca, Pocahontas met John Smith at a London party, she could not believe it. She was convinced he had died many years before in America as the result of an explosion.

North American tribes   Encampment in Virginia   Village of North American Indians

CONQUERORS
and
EXPLORERS

The indomitable king who conquered nations and lands across the known world

ALEXANDER THE GREAT

(Macedonia 356 BC – Babylon 323 BC)

The tent hooks rattled gently in the breeze which blew in from across the plain. A strange silence spread around the bare furnishings, from the armour, now cast to one side, to the mat on the ground. In the shadows, a man was staring at a map. But instead of the signs and the shapes on the parchment, he was seeing green landscapes, snow-covered slopes, raging rivers and calm stretches of water, then armies preparing to go into battle, attacks on horseback and great banquets to celebrate victory. At last, Alexander lifted his head towards a patch of sunlight as the camp began to come alive. Next day, the road would lead him back the way he had come – no more unknown lands, but familiar paths leading at last to the royal palace. It was 324 BC and for the first time in his life, Alexander the Great was tasting defeat. Betrayed by his soldiers, he now had to return home to Babylon without having realized his dream of conquering the whole world.

Part of the *Olympiad*, written by Aristotle

Delirious and weakened by fever, Alexander the Great passed away on June 10, 323 BC. This was the year following the mutiny of his army, when the soldiers who had been with him throughout his long campaign to conquer the eastern world, made up their minds to return home. In just thirty years, from 336 BC when he had acceded to the throne of Macedonia, following his father, **Philip II**, Alexander had succeeded in creating an immense empire which extended across all the lands from Greece to India. Alexander had dreamed of ruling the world almost from the day he was born in 356 BC in Pella (Macedonia). His father Philip II, as well as being king, was also a brave warrior, and Alexander's mother **Olympias** was determined that her son would be the same. Alexander first went into battle when he was only sixteen years old. By 338 BC Alexander had become leader of the cavalry (soldiers on horseback), leading them to victory at Chaeronea against the Thebans and the Athenians, a conquest which enabled Philip II to rule the whole of Greece. Alexander became king in 336 BC and became leader of the city-states of Greece by controlling the League of Corinth, setting his sights on expansion towards Egypt, a land which he conquered without any bloodshed five years later in 331 BC. Here Alexander was crowned pharaoh – not only the crowned king, but also called by the Egyptian priests the son of Amon-Ra, the Sun god, and he founded Alexandria, the first of a long line of cities to bear Alexander's name.

At this point, Alexander saw his progress towards the east opening up, once he had fought off the armies of the Persian Emperor, Darius III. The decisive battle was fought on the plain of **Gaugamela** in 331 BC. After that, Darius was forced to flee, leaving Alexander to enter Babylon as the victor. After a short rest in what was then the capital of Persia, Alexander moved his army further eastward, discovering places which were previously unknown in the west, except in myths and legends – such as Scythia (now part of Russia) and Bactria, India (present-day Afghanistan).

The crossing of the **River Hybhasis** in 324 BC was the last stop on this long journey. Now, Alexander's troops, who had been marching and fighting for many years since leaving Macedonia, rebelled and Alexander had to retreat back towards Persia, first to the city of Susa and then Babylon. It was here that Alexander died, whilst he was planning to re-organize his army ready to invade the Arab coast of the Persian Gulf.

Alexander and Philip shown in a miniature

A throne stained with blood

Philip II, Alexander's father, was killed in 336 BC. His actual murderer, one of Philip's officers called Pausanius, confessed to the crime and although he was punished, there were many rumours about those who must have been part of the **conspiracy**.

Many people wanted Philip dead, and for many reasons.

Olympias, Philip's divorced wife and mother of Alexander, was suspected of taking part in the plotting of her husband's murder, and many believed that she had lied about a conflict with her son.

Her conduct afterwards certainly showed her to be a cold, ruthless woman. First, she killed Cleopatra, Philip's widow and her children, so that Alexander would be the only true heir – his only rival for the throne was Philip's son Arrhidaeus (Alexander's half-brother) who was mentally subnormal. So, by her cruel deeds, Olympias made it easy for Alexander to accede to the throne of Macedonia.

The wives of Alexander

Alexander saw marriage as a way of strengthening his power over nations both in the western and the eastern world, as well as bringing countries together. So, although some of his subjects who were Macedonian hoped that he would marry a Greek woman, his first marriage was to **Barsine**, daughter of a Persian nobleman. She was followed in 327 BC by **Roxana**, born in Bactria (now, Afghanistan) a region which

Alexander had only partly conquered. In 324 BC at Susa she organized a spectacular celebration, with thousands of pages and about eighty knights each marrying a Persian woman. On this occasion, Alexander also took two Asian princesses as wives – **Statira**, daughter of the deposed Darius III and **Parysatis**, heiress to Artaxerxes III.

Wedding of Alexander and Statira, from a fresco at Pompeii

A philosopher in the company of a king

Marble bust of Aristotle

In 343 BC, **Aristotle**, the Greek philosopher (great thinker) arrived in the city of Pella, capital of Macedonia and seat of the royal court. Aristotle was a famous person mostly due to his writings on human behaviour and astronomy. He had also calculated the Olympiad, the four-yearly intervals between Olympic games, by which it was possible to calculate the years. He had been asked by Philip II, the Macedonian king, to take charge of the education of Alexander, Philip's son and the probable heir to the throne. Aristotle encouraged Alexander to discover new things and continually widen his knowledge, and his teaching was something which deeply affected Alexander for the whole of his life – shown by the fact that his conquests were mostly the result of a desire to explore new lands and to meet unknown populations. But Aristotle and Alexander disagreed sharply about one thing, which was Alexander's habit of adopting habits and rituals from the lands and the people which he had conquered. Aristotle totally disapproved of this, believing in the superiority of the Greeks to the 'barbarians' (non-Greeks).

An invincible formation

The military successes of Philip II, first, and then his son Alexander, were due to a large extent to the skill and efficiency of their troops in battle. The main nucleus of the army was the infantry (soldiers on foot) arranged in close formation, each man armed with a shield and a long lance, to form a compact square. The front lines advanced horizontally, aiming to hit the most enemies as quickly as possible. Those enemies who managed to run from this front line attack would usually fall on the dead bodies of their fellow soldiers and would be hit by the following lines of attacking troops. At the sides of this compact square would be the cavalry (horseback soldiers) of select warriors called the **hetairos** (king's companions). Their task was to protect the sides of the infantry and to carry out rapid assaults in the field of the enemy.

Hero or tyrant?

Alexander was often worshipped as a hero who fought for his people, and often accused of being a bloodthirsty dictator. In both cases, there was some truth. Alexander was a courageous man, ready to fight with his troops in the front line of battle. He is known to have been generous in sharing loot taken from the enemy, and a man interested in geography, history and literature who never accepted half-measures or compromise. There are also many stories told about the darker side of his personality – a man who was often drunk, with a fierce temper and a cruel streak which he made no attempt to hide. In battle, Alexander's life had been saved by his General, Clitus. Yet, when he was drunk, he was capable of killing Clitus without mercy, and immediately demanded the death of anyone he imagined was trying to cheat him in any way. For instance, he sought a bloodthirsty revenge on men such as his close friend Philotas, his most brave general, Parmenion, and Callisthenes, grandson of his teacher Aristotle.

Alexander and Darius in battle

Generals, assassins and the king

The immense kingdom which Alexander had created did not survive after his death. For a short time, Antigonus, Seleucus, Cassander, Ptolemy and Lysimachus, all important members of the Macedonian army, succeeded in sharing out a vast expanse of land, but the battle for power was always being fought in many ways and at the cost of enormous losses. **Cassander** was particularly ruthless in putting to death every person who had any claim at all to the throne of Macedonia. In 316 BC he assassinated Alexander's mother, **Olympias**, and in 310 BC killed the only son of Alexander the Great, Alexander IV, together with his mother, **Roxana**. But in other cases, the transition from the rule of Alexander to that of the successor was less bloody. Ptolemy, for example, installed himself in Egypt without difficulty, becoming the forefather of a royal house of pharaohs, which only ended with the death of Ptolemy XV (son of **Cleopatra**) in 30 BC, when Augustus the future Emperor of Rome, came to the Egyptian throne.

Ptolemy, Alexander's General and Egyptian Pharaoh

Poison of the Mosquito

The death of Alexander the Great remains a mystery to this day. What caused such a young, strong man who had led an army to conquer the whole world to die at the age of only thirty three? There were so many plots among Alexander's generals to seize power from him that he always feared more plots and attacks. But because Alexander had changed from a brave conquerer to a cruel dictator, many people jumped to the conclusion that he must have been poisoned. Other ancient historians believed that death had been due to an excess of alcohol in the last days of Alexander's life. It is said that he could drink five litres of pure wine, undiluted with water, in one sitting. More recently, some American researchers have advanced the theory that the **mosquito** of the genus *Culex* could have been responsible for the death of the Macedonian king by the transmission of a lethal virus, the **Virus of the Western Nile** which causes brain fever and, if it is not cured, death.

The king on his throne, from a version of the book the *Alexander Romance*

UNPOPULAR CUSTOMS
When he became ruler of Persia, Alexander adopted some eastern rituals and traditions which his forces disliked intensely. The most hated was the humiliating custom of having to prostrate themselves on the ground in front of Alexander, as if he were a god.

Mosquito larvae

*The Roman General who created the
basis for the birth of an empire*

GAIUS JULIUS CAESAR
(Rome 101 BC – 44 BC)

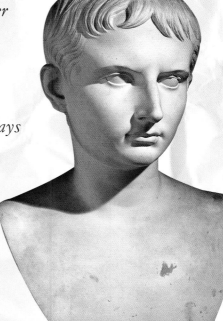

*For hours, Caesar had been watching the Rubicon river, the river
which marked the boundary between Gaul and Italy. The
soldiers drawn up behind him were waiting for a sign from him
to ford the river on their horses and make their way through
Italy and into Rome. But each time he drew breath to issue a
command to his troops, the words choked in his throat. Three days
earlier he had fought the enemy: the next step was to cross the
Rubicon, to face another enemy in Italy. Julius Caesar did
not fear the justice of the senate or the gods. He did not fear
battles with the army of Pompey (Gnaeus Pompeius). What
concerned him most was his loyalty to the traditions of the
Republic of Rome. But this was no time to hesitate. Taking
a deep breath, he spurred his horse into a gallop through the
river, to the cries of war from his men behind him.*

In January 49 BC, Julius Caesar led his army across the
Rubicon river which divided Gaul (today the alpine region of northern Italy and southern
France) from Italy. For many years, this Roman General had been occupied in many campaigns
against Gaul. By crossing the Rubicon, he was preparing to conquer Rome and rise to power.
Julius Caesar was born in Rome in 101 BC into a family of ancient nobility. During the rule of the
dictator **Lucius Cornelius Sulla** (82–79 BC), Caesar was forced to flee from Italy. To escape from
Sulla, he enlisted in an army which was serving in Asia. When Sulla died, it became possible for
Julius Caesar to return to Rome and resume his career as a statesman. After going to Rhodes to
study the **art of oratory** (the skill of speaking in public) in 68 BC, he was appointed **quaestor**
(chief law-keeper) of the province of 'Farther Spain' (now Southern Spain and Portugal), and this

The River Rubicon in Northern Italy　　　　　The Roman Senate in a painting by Cesare Maccari

Triumphal Arch in honour of Julius Caesar

position meant that he could enter the Senate (the Roman council). His first appearance as a statesman was in 63 BC, with his election to the important position of Pontefiex Maximus (High Priest). But there was still a good deal of discontent and disagreements to be resolved following the dictatorship of Sulla. Julius Caesar's skills were put to the test with the so-called '**first triumvirate**' an agreement drawn up between Caesar, Roman statesman Marcus Licinius Crassus and **Pompey**. This agreement divided the Roman territory between the three men. Caesar had the command of Roman **Gaul** as Pro Consul (Governor). After having successfully commanded numerous battles (from 58 BC – 52 BC) against the Gaul people who had not yet surrendered, Caesar revealed his intention of entering Rome with his own troops in 49 BC. The following year, with the victory of Pharmaceo against Pompey, he became the absolute chief of the Roman Republic. Now, Caesar was a powerful man, and he had many rivals. It was his relationship with the Egyptian queen **Cleopatra** as well as his insistence on total command which attracted the hatred of many Roman nobles, some of whom gathered together in a conspiracy to assassinate him. On 15th (the ides) of March 44 BC, as he was leaving the Senate House, Caesar was killed by three stab wounds.

Basalt statue of Cleopatra

The Myth of Cleopatra

The figure of Cleopatra (*circa* 69 BC – 30 BC) has fascinated writers, poets and dramatists from ancient times. She was the heroine of the Shakespeare tragedy *Antony and Cleopatra*, and the epic 1963 film starring Elizabeth Taylor. There were many different aspects to the personality of the last queen of Egypt. Although she inherited the throne through Egyptian pharaohs, she was, in fact, Macedonian, and felt she had been called to reign over a kingdom greater than Egypt. She was worshipped as the living re-birth of the Egyptian goddess Iside, but although she was not particularly beautiful, she fascinated two brave Roman generals, Caesar and Mark Antony, causing the ruin of both.

When she died, killing herself by the bite of a poisonous asp, the Egyptians lost not only a fatally attractive woman, but also the mysterious and age-old world of the pharaohs and the dream of a universal empire – the same concept which was in the mind of the Macedonian conqueror, Alexander the Great.

Poster for the film *Cleopatra*

Caesar in Literature

Caesar was not only a courageous general and a clever politician, he was also a gifted **narrator** (story-teller). In the years between 58 and 52 BC, whilst he held control of the people of Gaul, he wrote a series of reports on his expeditions which he then put together in a work entitled *Commentaries of the Beautiful Gaul* – a valuable source of information on the habits and customs of various tribes which he met in battle and that were conquered by his army. In three books which he compiled entitled *Commentaries of Beautiful Civilizations* Julius Caesar tried to justify the Roman battles which he had seen and taken part in, often using sarcasm to criticize the soldiers led by Pompey, who had fought against him.

Divine origins

Below, Aeneas, fleeing from Troy; right, the Venus de Milo

The complete name for Julius Caesar was **Gaius**, meaning 'father', **Julius**, after his 'gens' or 'clan' name the Julii, and Caesar, his own family name. He belonged to a famous noble family and could boast many renowned ancestors, such as Julius Ascanius founder of the Roman city of Alba Longa. According to legend, Ascanius was the son of Aeneas, the Trojan hero who was the son of the beautiful goddess **Venus** and the mortal Anchises. This made Julius Caesar believe that he was a descendant of the gods, and he always honoured Venus, even building a temple dedicated to the goddess.

A brave enemy

One particularly important episode in the life of Julius Caesar was the conflict with **Vercingetorix**, chief of the Arverni tribe in Gaul. Vercingetorix had called together different Gallic tribes, stirring them up to fight Julius Caesar's army in order to free themselves from Roman occupation. The Bituriges tribe prepared their town Avaricum (now Bourges, east central France) for a siege against an enemy attack, but this was useless against Julius Caesar's army. When Alesia (52 BC) was also defeated after a fierce battle, Vercingetorix surrendered and was taken to Rome by Julius Caesar as a prisoner. In 46 BC, Caesar was given absolute command of the whole of Gaul, making his victories even more triumphant. Vercingetorix was taken in chains along the road to Rome. Soon after his arrival there, he was killed.

Death of Julius Caesar by Vincenzo Camuccini

Sayings which became famous

Veni, vidi, vici 'I came, I saw, I conquered'. Julius Caesar is said to have uttered these words at the end of his campaign against the Asiatic king Pharnaces II defeated in an epic battle at Zela (47 BC). ***Tu quoque, Brute, filii mii;*** ' You as well, Brutus, my own son'. This phrase was said by Julius Caesar at the point of death, when he saw that Marcus Brutus (85 – 42 BC), his adopted son, was among the conspirators. ***Alea iacta est.*** 'the die is cast' – the words of Julius Caesar at the moment of crossing the Rubicon River.

Transformation of a name

The word 'emperor' normally came to be associated with the image of an actual king – famous men such as Augustus, Tiberius, Nero, or, moving forward in history, Charlemagne, Charles V, Frederick II ...

When Rome became a Republic, the title 'emperor' was also given to generals who had achieved notable victories.

These two meanings became linked due to Julius Caesar – because as well as being a ruler, he had also achieved many important victories on the battlefield.

The Reform of Time

From 46 BC, Julius Caesar decreed that the number of days in a year should be increased from 355 to 365. The new calculation of the yearly calendar, named 'Julian' in his honour, remained in force until 1582, when **Pope Gregory XII** changed it slightly and originated the '**Gregorian**' calendar, which is still in use.

Left, gold coins with the image and name of Julius Caesar
Below, a London production of the play *Julius Caesar* by William Shakespeare

The peasant girl warrior who fought for the freedom of France

JOAN OF ARC
(Domremy circa 1412 – Rouen 1431)

The old market square at Rouen was packed. During the previous night, a pile of wooden stakes had been heaped up at the centre. Now, the crowd silently made a path for a young girl to pass through towards the scaffold, poorly dressed in a habit rather like a nun's. The English garrison faced with the task of putting the girl to death, had every kind of insult from the crowd, many of whom had been there for hours. But the girl did not seem to pay any attention to her surroundings. Suddenly, the flames began to burn the hem of her dress. The heat flared up, as the fire slowly began to destroy her body. The girl cried out, but not with distress; instead she called on the angels, the saints, the Virgin Mary. A priest held a crucifix to her face. Soon, both had disappeared into the fire, and the name of Jesus, whispered with her last breath, dissolved into the crackling of the flames.

On 30 May 1431, Joan of Arc was burned alive in the main square of the French city of Rouen, accused of witchcraft. She was a young girl, about eighteen years old, who, in the short space of just one year, had changed the fate of her country, France. Joan was born, probably in 1412, into a peasant family in Domrémy, a village which during the Hundred Years War supported the Dauphin (heir to the French throne) the future **Charles VII**, against the occupying English forces of Henry VI. At thirteen years of age, Joan was promised in marriage, as was the custom at the time. But her life was

Joan of Arc liberates Orléans

Joan of Arc enters Orléans

to take a different course. She began to hear the **voices of the saints and archangels**, which told her that she must free France from the English and put Charles on the French throne. The story of this child, who had been given a task from heaven, soon spread throughout the country. From then on, Joan was known as the 'Maid of La Pucelle'. After many attempts, she was received by Charles in the castle of Chinon in March 1429. Incredibly, the dauphin decided to give to this girl, a peasant who, until that moment had not even used any weapons, the command of an army. Almost immediately, Joan marched towards the city of Orléans, which, for many months, had been under siege by the English armies of Henry IV and liberated it. Events then developed rapidly: on 12 June, she regained the fortress of Jargeau; on 18 June, she conquered Patay and on 17 July 1429 she organized the coronation of Charles VII in the cathedral at Reims. Soon after, Joan's army suffered a harsh defeat just outside Paris and she was captured on 23 May 1430 by a band of French people who did not want Charles VII to be king. They handed her over to the English who tried her as a witch and condemned her to be burned in 1431.

English ship during the Hundred Years War

Supernatural voices

The childhood of Joan of Arc was identical to other children in Domrémy. Her first games in the open air would have been 'let's pretend'. Every young girl did household tasks to help their family – cooking, sewing, and most probably the care of domestic animals. At thirteen years old (the age at which a girl became an adult) something happened which affected her whole life. It was noon on a warm summer's day in 1425 when, as she passed in front of her home, she said that she clearly heard voices pleading with her to liberate France from the English armies. Remembering the events of this day, Joan later insisted that she had heard heavenly voices – those of **Saint Michael the Archangel, Saint Catherine** and **Saint Margaret**.

Icon representing Michael the Archangel

The navigator who went to find a passage to India and discovered the 'New World'

CHRISTOPHER COLUMBUS

(Genoa 1451 – Valladolid 1506)

Another day was breaking with no sign of land on the horizon. Standing on the bridge of his ship, Christopher Columbus glanced back at the two caravels following him. He could sense the unrest among the crew. Although none of the men had questioned his leadership, mutterings and complaints had increased with every hour that passed. He had been almost sure that they would soon reach India in a day or so, perhaps only a few hours. Now he was quite certain, not only because he had seen twigs floating on the water and birds which he knew stayed near the coastline, but he could also smell the scent of sand in the air. After what had seemed an age sailing across the ocean, now land could not be far away!

Until 12 October 1492, the expedition led by Christopher Columbus in search of a sea passage to **India** seemed a failure. After the three ships (two caravels, the *Niña* and the *Pinta*, and a flagship the *Santa Maria*) had left the Spanish port of Palos on 3 August, they had become trapped for weeks in the algae of the **Sargasso Sea**. At last, they worked the ships free, sailing for day after day without seeing land, not even the branch of a tree carried along by the current. Then, at two o'clock on the morning of 12 October, there came the cry of 'Land ahead!' from Rodrigo de Triana, a sailor on the *Pinta*.

A few hours later, they landed on an island. Columbus gave it the name of San Salvador and almost immediately embarked on a project which had been in his mind since boyhood. Growing up among

Christopher Columbus at the court of the Spanish King and Queen

Columbus with his son outside the convent of La Rabida

King Ferdinand's permission for Columbus to undertake his voyage

the alleyways of Genoa, the city where he had been born in 1451, he had gone to sea when he was little more than a child. Sailing on ships which crossed the Mediterranean Sea between 1474 and 1476, he had sometimes landed on Chios, a Greek island which had built up many trading contacts with merchant ships from the east. But it was towards Iceland that Columbus sailed in 1476, inspired perhaps by tales of the Vikings, those brave, fearless sea warriors of the Norse lands. But, Columbus never forgot his visits to Chios. He studied the writings of **Marco Polo** who had travelled to China centuries before, and pored over the charts and the maps of famous astronomers, trying to see if it could be possible to reach Cathay (China) from the west, across the Atlantic Ocean. But such an expedition would cost money and Columbus would also need the support of a powerful monarch before he could sail to unknown lands. First, he went to the Portuguese Court of **John II** in 1483, but he was refused. Columbus then went to the Spanish king and queen, **Ferdinand** and **Isabella**, and it was Ferdinand who agreed to finance the voyage. After seven long years of meetings, trials and setbacks, from 1486 to 1492, everything was ready for Columbus to set sail. The voyage of Columbus to what he called the 'West Indies' (he did not even know that he had discovered a new continent) was a great success.

Columbus became so admired that he took charge of the lands which he explored, and Ferdinand gave him money for seventeen ships for a second voyage. This was followed by another two voyages, but neither was as happy or so successful as the first. The growing demand for Spanish **colonies** (lands governed by Spain) caused resentment among the native people and this led to revolt against the European explorers, often death. At the end of his third exploration, Columbus was taken back to Spain in chains; his poor management of the new colony was seen as the cause for the small amount of gold coming back from the West Indies. He was soon freed, but never regained his earlier popularity. After returning to the 'New World' for a fourth time, he died in 1505, alone and his death going almost unnoticed.

A world of new discoveries

Like many other explorers, Columbus was always searching for gold and aromatic spices – and he was sure he would find them when he reached India. Instead, in the 'New World' he discovered products which in many cases would prove as valuable as gold – sometimes more valuable, as our use of them centuries after his voyages has proved.

Potato – once seen as 'the fruit of the devil', because it grows under the soil, this vegetable was first used only to feed prisoners.

Corn – also called 'maize'. In Italian (the language of Columbus), this is called 'granturco' meaning 'large Turk'; and anything Turkish was seen as strange and foreign.

Cocoa – the ancient Mayan and Aztec civilizations used the seeds of this plant to make chocolate, which they used for their ceremonies and rituals.

Rubber – the native people obtained this from the plant *Hevea brasiliensis*, and used rubber to make balls with which they played a game rather like lacrosse.

Tobacco – with the leaves of this herbal plant, the native people made a type of cigar, which they lit at one end and smoked. This habit was soon copied by the western explorers.

Thousands of sea voyages

The fifteenth and the sixteenth centuries were times of great explorations. During this time there were a number of fearless navigators, who defied ignorance and superstition and made sensational discoveries. With each of their voyages, people in Europe became excited and often frightened that there could be places which, until then, they could not have imagined.

JOHN CABOT
(circa 1450 – 1498)
arrived at what is now Canada in 1497. The following year, he continued his exploration towards Labrador.

BARTHOLOMEW DIAZ
(1450 – 1500)
discovered the **Cape of Good Hope** at the southernmost point of the African continent (1487 – 1488).

VASCO DE GAMA
(1469 – 1524)
was the first to reach Calcutta, India, by sea (1497 – 1499) sailing around the **Cape of Good Hope**.

FERDINAND MAGELLAN
(1480 – 1521)
discovered the **straits** which separate South America from the islands of Tierra del Fuego and the Pacific Ocean (1520). *Victoria*, the only ship from his expedition to survive the long voyage, returned to Europe in 1522, captained by Juan Sebastián Elcano (circa 1476 – 1526), completing the first **circumnavigation of the world**. Magellan had been killed the year before in the Philippines.

The explorer who became a hero and lost his life near the South Pole

ROBERT FALCON SCOTT
(Devonport 1846 – Antarctic 1912)

The whole tent shook violently under the onslaught of the severe snow storm. Inside, there was a deep silence. The faithful Wilson, who until the very last moment had not lost hope or faith in his leader, had not spoken for hours, whilst 'Birdie' Bowers lay quite still, rolled up in fur. The heavy burden of defeat and failure rested on the shoulders of Captain Robert Scott, head of the expedition. His limbs were completely numb and he was sleepy. But he dare not shut his eyes for fear of never waking up. Instead he continued to fight what he knew was his forthcoming death. With his last ounce of energy, he reached for his diary and with a shaking hand wrote his last message. 'Every day we have been ready to start for our depot 11 miles away, but outside the door of the tent it remains a scene of whirling drift … We shall stick it out to the end, but we are getting weaker, of course, and the end cannot be far.'

The diary with the 'message to the public' of Captain Robert Falcon Scott, who left for a scientific expedition to the Antarctic at the end of 1911, was found near his body by an English rescue team on 12 November 1912 (about eight months after his death). The news of his death and four of his companions reached Europe a few months after, in February 1913, when it had already become known that the South Pole had been conquered by the

Norwegian **Roald Engelbert Amundsen** on 14 December 1911. For Scott, the challenge of the Antarctic had begun years before in 1900, when he had been chosen to lead a scientific exploration to the Antarctic Polar Circle. When he left in 1901, he was unprepared for the harsh climate and conditions of the Antarctic ice cap. Until then he had been a **naval captain**, skilled in seamanship from a young age, but without experience in handling the necessary equipment and surviving in Antarctica. Yet, despite these limitations, Scott's first exploration proved to be an incredible success and he became famous. Even so, Scott still felt that he had further work to do in the Antarctic. So, at the end of 1909, after he had raised enough money, Scott organized a second expedition. This time,

it would not be limited to **scientific research**, he would also try to reach the **South Pole**. The long, exhausting walk on foot, which in the end proved fatal, began in November 1911. But when Scott and his party reached the Pole, they found that Amundsen had already been there. Despite the bitter disappointment, Scott and his men undertook what had been the main purpose of the expedition – collecting biological and geological samples. At 17 kilometres from the base camp, where they would have been able to find enough fuel and food to keep everyone alive, Scott and his party were trapped by a terrible blizzard. All died from exposure within a few days. It was March 1912.

Left-hand page, bottom: the polar ice cap

Top: a member of Scott's expedition team

Above, an immense block of ice

Below, base camp during one of the stages of Scott's expedition

Right, Robert Edwin Peary, the first man to reach the North Pole

Peary, with his husky dog

Amundsen, beside the Norwegian flag

Amundsen, the winner who was finally beaten

Roald Engelbert Amundsen (1872 – 1928) was born and grew up in the cold land of Norway, and so the icy expanses of the North Pole did not frighten him. He was an immensely strong man, and as a boy he had journeyed on sledges pulled by teams of dogs at temperatures which were incredibly low. So, he was the ideal candidate for polar explorations. In November 1909, when he was ready to leave for the Arctic, he received the news that the American **Robert Edwin Peary** had already conquered the North Pole. But his disappointment did not last long. He decided to turn his attention to the Antarctic. This time, well ahead of the English expedition, he reached the South Pole in 1911. But, like Scott, a tragic fate awaited him. He met his death in 1928 trying to rescue the Italian explorer **Umberto Nobile** in an airship crash near Spitzbergen in the Arctic Circle. However, Nobile survived, and did not die until 1978 aged 93.

Statue of Peter Pen in Kensington Gardens, London

Signals requesting help after the crash of the airship *Italia*

The friend of Peter Pan

In 1909, whilst Scott was preparing for the expedition to reach the South Pole, his wife, the artist Kathleen Bruce, gave birth to a son. He was named Peter, after the main character in the story written in 1904 by James Matthew Barrie (1860 – 1937) – *Peter Pan, or the boy who never grew up*. The reason was that Captain Scott wanted to pay tribute to Barrie, because he, more than anyone else, had understood his aspirations and his dreams. In fact, Barrie described Scott as 'a strange mixture of a dreamer and a practical man'.

Members of Scott's expedition
with their husky dogs during a
moment of rest

Scott's ship trapped in the ice

Experiences of cold lands

At the beginning of the nineteenth century there was a great deal of interest in the **conquest of the North and South poles**. With the promise of grants from governments and scientific associations, many different types of people wanted to take part in polar explorations and for very different reasons. As well as explorers dedicated to scientific studies, there were also adventurers and sportsmen interested in achieving fame and glory. From their writings, often published after their death, their memories give an insight into their fascination with the cold and cruel climate of the North and South Poles, where a man had to prove his concern for his team-mates, his loyalty, courage and the spirit of sacrifice. These accounts include –

Robert F. Scott, *The Voyage of the Discovery* (1905)
Robert F. Scott, *The Last Expedition* (1931/1927)
Roald Amundsen, *The South Pole* (1912)
Apsley Cherry-Garrard, *The Worst Journey in the World* (1922)
Ernest H. Shackleton, *The Heart of the Antarctic* (1909)
Umberto Nobile, *The Red Tent. Memories of Snow and Fire* (1969)

Scott and his company
pulling the heavy sledges

All the numbers of an exploration

About 5 months passed from the departure to the end of the mission:

11 people had left with Scott – 7 were the support team. At the Beardmore Glacier, just 4 proceeded with Scott to the conquest of the South Pole (Edwin Adrian Wilson, Edgar Evans, Lawrence Oates and Henry Bowers)

16 kilogrammes of geological material (fossils and rocks) were collected during Scott's return journey;

17 kilometres separated the surviving members from those who perished.

The love of an artist

Scott's wife, **Kathleen Bruce** was seen as a modern woman, very much ahead of her time. In Paris she got to know and became a student of the artist Pablo Picasso and the sculptor Auguste Rodin. Before meeting her future husband, she toured Europe with her friend **Isadora Duncan**, the celebrated ballerina tragically killed in 1927 whilst motoring in the French Riviera – the long scarf which she had wound around her neck caught in the steering wheel of her sports car and killed her.

Isadora Duncan

The aviator who was the first to fly solo, non-stop from New York to Paris

CHARLES LINDBERGH

(Detroit 1902 – isola di Maui 1974)

In the cold light of the moon, the aircraft flew slowly across the ocean, just skimming over the water. Suddenly, it gained height, rising up into the night sky. Then, after having remained for a short time high above the sea, it fell again towards the waves. Determined not to lose his dream by falling asleep, the pilot, crouched in the tiny cockpit of his monoplane, had worked out a system to keep awake. If he dozed for a few seconds, then as the aircraft lost height, it would 'bounce' and make a bell ring to wake him. He could not afford to sleep – the coast of Ireland was very near. He could not remember the last time he had seen any fishing boats. In front of him stretched the vast expanse of ocean before land came in sight. His destination had not yet been reached, but his goal, Paris, was becoming ever nearer.

Ireland would have appeared like a dream to the tired eyes of Charles Lindbergh. About twenty five hours earlier, he had taken off from **Roosevelt Field** (New York) to complete what was seen as a foolhardy undertaking – to fly solo across the Atlantic Ocean and land at Paris. Right up until the moment of take-off on the morning of 20 May 1927, there seemed little chance of success for Lindbergh – so much so, that it had taken him a long time, not only to get the money to pay for the flight, but also to convince

someone to build a monoplane especially adapted for the flight. Despite these challenges, after 30 hours and 33 minutes, Lindbergh's monoplane *The Spirit of St. Louis* landed on the runway of Le Bourget airport (near Paris). Lindbergh, who was only twenty five years old, entered a new phase of his life: from an unknown airmail pilot flying from Chicago to St. Louis, he had become the most famous and admired person in the world.

Satellite photograph of St. Louis in Missouri

The son of a Swedish-born lawyer, Lindbergh abandoned his university studies in 1922 to follow his dream of flying, becoming first a **military pilot** (1924) and then a **postal pilot** (1926). But after he had achieved fame and wealth with his historic flight, a time of great sadness was to follow. Lindbergh's baby son, also named Charles, was abducted and murdered on the 2 March 1932. After this tragedy, he and his family moved to Europe to escape the attention of the American media. This was followed by Lindbergh's controversial visits to Nazi Germany, where he had meetings with important members of the German armed forces and appealed to the United States not to become involved in a second world war. All this made him far less popular in the eyes of the American public. However, when the United States did enter the war, Lindbergh became a **civil pilot**, and this restored his reputation to a great extent. Until his death in 1974, Lindbergh was an important member of many campaigns to do with nature and the environment, and in 1961 he became one of the founders of the World Wildlife Fund.

Anne Morrow, Lindbergh's wife

Lindbergh, the writer

In 1954, Charles Lindbergh achieved important literary recognition by winning the **Pulitzer Prize**. This was an honour bestowed on him not as a pilot, but as the author of his book, *The Spirit of St. Louis*. This was not his first book, but it was the most successful, attracting the approval of literary critics as well as the public. Lindbergh's book *The Solitary Eagle* which was written within a few months of his historical flight in 1927, sold thousands of copies, but the reasons for its success had been due more to the fame and glory of his incredible achievement than to the actual literary value of the work. Conversely, Lindbergh's wife, **Anne Morrow**, a talented writer, was not very popular with the public in comparison to her husband.

The monoplane *The Spirit of St. Louis* attracted the crowds

A cruel kidnap

The trial of what was at the time considered to be the '**crime of the century**' opened at the beginning of January 1935 before the court in Flemington, a small city in New Jersey. In the spring of 1932, the kidnap and murder of little **Charles junior**, son of the famous pilot Charles Lindbergh, had been committed. Despite Lindbergh paying a huge ransom, the baby, who was less than two years old, had been found dead on 9 May 1932, little more than two months from the day of the kidnapping (2 March). The person charged with the crime, German-born Richard (Bruno) Hauptmann, was caught trying to pay a bill with one of the notes Lindbergh had paid in ransom (the police had listed all the serial numbers) and Hauptmann was condemned to death on 6 April 1936.

The house where the kidnapping took place

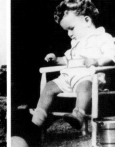
Charles junior

police surveys

From aircraft to the heart

Despite not having finished his university studies, Lindbergh learned to invent and to build gadgets for his aircraft. His interests in this direction also extended to medicine – an area apparently quite removed from his own field of expertise. Together with Doctor **Alexis Carrel** (1873 – 1944) who became his close friend, Lindbergh invented a **mechnical pump** which made it possible for blood to circulate around the body, doing the job of a human heart (1934 – 1935).

Failures before Lindbergh

In 1919, the American magnate Raymond Orteig offered a prize of 25,000 dollars to anyone who could succeed in flying from Paris to New York, or vice versa. At the beginning of 1926, with more reliable and powerful aircraft becoming available, many people decided to try for the prize. First to try, in 1926, was the French pilot **René Fonck**. Unfortunately, his aircraft did not even take off. Instead, it crashed at the end of the runway, causing the death of two members of the team. But the series of accidents was not yet finished. In 1927, during some test flights, the American aviator **Richard Byrd** was killed, as well as two other pilots, **Noel Davis** and **Stanton Webster**. The partnership of the experienced French aviators **Charles Nungesser** and **François Coli** with their aircraft *L'Oiseau Blanc* (White Bird) seemed destined for greater glories. Sadly, they were lost at sea on 8 May 1927.

Parade through New York in honour of Charles Lindbergh

Statistics of an aircraft

NAME: *Ryan NYP* ('**RYAN**' indicates the maker: **NY** stands for the place of departure, New York: and P signals the destination, Paris) – better known as the *Spirit of St. Louis*, which Lindbergh named after the American city which gave money towards the flight.

REGISTRATION NUMBER: *N-X-211* (**N** was the sign given to all aircraft registered in the United States and **X** indicates an experimental aircraft.)

COST: 10,580 dollars

ENGINE: radial (nine cylinders arranged in a wheel pattern) with 223 horsepower

QUANTITY OF FUEL: about 1800 litres

SIZE OF COCKPIT: tiny – (just enough space for a man) to save on fuel

BELONGINGS: kept to a minimum, just documents, a little money, two bottles of water and five rolls (being alone, Lindbergh did not eat much!)

AVERAGE SPEED: 170 kilometres per hour

DISTANCE COVERED: about 5,760 kilometres

TIME TAKEN: 33 hours and 30 minutes

Lindbergh in front of the *Spirit of St. Louis* on the runway of Roosevelt Field

The explorer of the Pacific Ocean who was assassinated by Hawaiian natives

JAMES COOK

(Marton, Cleveland 1728 – Hawaii 1779)

James Cook, the explorer who for many years had sailed the Pacific Ocean in search of new lands, met his death on the island of Sandwich (now, Hawaii) in 1779. At the time of his landing at **Kealakekua** in January of the same year, the local people had welcomed the English captain as if he were a god. But soon there was deep unrest between the natives and the western exploration team.

During an argument on the beach, Cook was attacked and killed. Members of his crew managed to save only a few of his bones.

In contrast to many navigators who sailed the oceans in search of fame and riches, Cook had undertaken his sea voyages attracted by a deep desire to make new discoveries. A student of astronomy and a skilled chart-maker, in 1768, he was chosen to command an expedition to Tahiti, where he reported on a rare astronomical event – the conjunction of the planet Venus with the Sun. During the three expeditions undertaken in the Australian seas (1768 – 1771; 1772 – 1775 and 1776 – 1779) he discovered **New Caledonia**, the islands in Polynesia which took his name (now the **Cook Islands**), and the **Sandwich Archipelago**, named after his friend the Count of Sandwich (who also 'invented' the sandwich!) Arriving at the coast of **Australia**, he claimed dominion of these territories in the name of the British crown.

A mysterious disappearance

Michael Rockefeller (1938 – 1961), heir to a powerful family of American oil magnates, disappeared in 1961 at only twenty three years old in New Guinea, where he had gone to study and collect works of art of the **Asmati natives**. Since then, many people have tried to explain what happened to him, but without any evidence. Some people believed he had drowned, others said he must have been killed by a shark – or that he had simply decided to live with the natives. The most fascinating theory, and the most sinister, is that he was captured and killed by cannibals as part of a macabre ritual. In 1969, the **Michael Rockefeller Art Center** was founded in his honour, and it is here that works of art by the people of New Guinea are exhibited.

Top right, a native of Papua New Guinea:
bottom right, an Asmati man building a boat

READ ALL ABOUT IT:
Milt Machlin wrote a book about the disappearance of Michael Rockefeller, entitled **In Search of Michael Rockefeller** *(2000).*

ARTISTS
and
SCULPTORS

The Greek sculptor who astounded the world with the majesty of his statues

PHIDIAS
(circa 490 BC – circa 430 BC)

The dying rays of the Sun skimmed over the smooth surface of the marble, making it glow pink and red. Another day had set on the mound of the Acropolis at the centre of Athens. Now, workmen were laying down their tools, ready to leave for their homes before nightfall. This was the time of silence, the sky and the earth almost seemed to be one. In the final moments before darkness fell, Phidias stood quite still looking across the city now specked with the lights from the torches which were already being lit. This was the time when Phidias the sculptor became Phidias the god-like creator. In his mind he could see centaurs, giants, amazons, heroes and gods ready to be sculpted next day from stone.

The dates regarding the life of Phidias are uncertain. Many of the works of art which he is believed to have done have vanished with the passage of time – destroyed by fire, damaged by acts of vandalism or simply reduced to dust over the centuries. Yet, based on the few surviving fragments of sculpture, the words of people living at the same time, and copies made during the times of the ancient Romans, he was obviously the greatest sculptor in ancient history.

Phidias was born in Athens, somewhere around 490 BC. First he worked as a painter, but he soon abandoned this in order to become a sculptor. Within a short time, his first statues were seen as works of art in a completely new style, later known as 'classical Phidias'. He was a friend of **Pericles**, a famous and powerful Athens statesman, for over thirty years, and it was Pericles who appointed Phidias in 447 BC to supervise the building of the **Parthenon**, a temple to be dedicated to the goddess Athena. In 437 BC, one year after the consecration of his statue, the **Athena Parthenos** for the central room of the temple, Phidias left Athens for the Greek city of Olympia. Here he sculpted the colossal statue of **Zeus**.

In 432 BC, Phidias was unjustly accused on two counts – first, of stealing some of the gold which was to be used in one of his statues, and second, of comparing himself to a god by depicting his own

Roman copy of the statue Athena Parthenos

Phidias presents his work to Pericles

image on the shield held by the goddess Athena. After then, nothing more is known about him. Some historians say he was imprisoned, and then fled after he served his sentence. Others say that Phidias died, or that he went far away, leaving Athens for ever.

The interest of Phidias in the human form was twofold: first, in his statues, he was always seeking to portray the various parts of the body and the whole body in perfect proportion. Second, he studied the pose and the expression of each part of the body, in order to portray not just the body itself, but the emotions he imagined to be inside, just as if his statues were real, living people.

Part of a statue from the temple of Athena

A god in gold and ivory

By 437 BC, Phidias was a famous man, celebrated for his ability to create **colossal statues** which he built using gold and ivory. So, he was the obvious choice when the Greek city of Olympia wanted an impressive statue of the god Zeus. Phidias sculpted his famous *Zeus Olympus*, a statue 14 metres high and which he created by covering a wooden framework with finely chiselled ivory and draperies in solid gold. For centuries this work has been considered one of the seven wonders of the world, yet is recorded only through the writings of some Greek and Latin writers, such as Strabo and Cicero. It was brought to Constantinople (now Istanbul), where it was destroyed by fire in 462 AD.

The temple of the city of Olympia

Pericles

The time during which Phidias lived and worked was also an age when both trade and art were flourishing in Athens. This age of prosperity was when **Pericles** (*circa* 495 BC – 429 BC) came to power as leader of the democratic party. His aim was to establish Athens as the political and cultural centre for the whole of Greece. Pericles achieved this, not by force, but through art. Some of the greatest works of art and intellect were created during the years of his government (463 BC – 430 BC), including the sculptures of Phidias,

the complex art and architecture of the Acropolis and the tragedy plays written by the great writer, **Sophocles**.

The temple of Athena

The temple of Athena was built with fifteen years of uninterrupted work, from 447 BC – 432 BC. It was an enormous commitment, paid for mainly by the Athenian government who wanted a temple built in honour of the goddess Athena on the Acropolis (the highest point in Athens). The architectural work was done by Ichtinus and Callicrates, whilst Phidias had the task of ornamenting the building. But even for an artist of his genius, the entire decoration of the Parthenon would be impossible for one man to do. And so he was helped in the sculptures by his students, making sure that they kept to his style of grace and perfect proportion, just as he did in his own work. Phidias did two works completely on his own – the statue of *Athena Promachos*, which he sculpted in bronze and erected at the entrance to the Acropolis, and that of *Athena Parthenos* in gold and ivory, placed at the centre of the Parthenon.

Pericles, fresco by Perugino

The Parthenon

The artist whose genius made religious and legendary subjects appear as real people

GIOTTO
(Colle di Vespignano, circa 1267 – Florence 1337)

This fresco painting would be his last work. Giotto examined closely the scene which had just been prepared by his students. There, on the plaster, smoothed carefully and then dampened, the subjects had been drawn with skill and the first layers of colours were dazzling. His teaching had borne good fruit. Now, he could be sure that his art would continue. The old master drew his brushes across the plaster, tracing colours along the shape of the eyes, then on the faces, along the folds of their clothes and on various features of the scenery in the background. Under the expert hand of the artist Giotto, the fresco seemed to come alive, as if the people in the painting were real, telling the story of the artist's life.

His name is thought to have been Ambrogiotto di Bondone – 'Giotto' was a shortened version. He was born into a peasant family at Colle di Vespignano in Mugello, a prosperous district on the outskirts of Florence. At an early age, probably only ten years old, Giotto became the errand boy in the art studio of the famous artist Bencivieni di Pepo, known as **Cimabue**. The artistic development of Giotto, as well as his students, was influenced by a journey to Rome during the years between 1285 and 1288, where he met and worked with the leading artists and sculptors of the day. Also, the example set by such an outstanding artist like Cimabue inspired in Giotto the search for his own artistic style. This style, he knew, would be directed towards more realism and most of all, great attention to the perspective – depth and distance in a painting. After having completed a series of frescos on the life of Saint Francis in the **Church of Saint**

Top, *Saint Francis receives the stigmata* by Van Eyck: bottom, the saint with the birds, painted by Giotto

Basilica of Saint Francis, Assisi

Francis in **Assisi** (1288 – 1300), Giotto became a famous artist and was asked to paint the altarpieces, crucifixes and paintings for many churches and chapels in many Italian cities – Rimini (*circa* 1301), Padua (1303 – 1304), Florence and Naples (1330 – 1333). To carry out the many works he was asked to do, Giotto made good use of skilled assistants, showing himself to be an excellent teacher as well as an artistic genius. He was also highly regarded as an architect and in 1334 he became responsible for designing the whole of the **Duomo** in Florence. Part of this vast undertaking was the bell tower, which, at his death (1337) was continued by **Andrea Pisano** and **Francesco Talenti** (from 1349).

Opinions of contemporaries

From the fourteenth century, Giotto was considered as the greatest artist who ever lived. According to the fifteenth century artist **Cennino Cennini**, Giotto had the genius to transform 'the art of painting from Greek into Latin' – that is, Giotto had abandoned the formal, impersonal style of Byzantine art (art of the Byzantine Empire, centred at Constantinople, now Istanbul, Turkey), to portray human expressions and emotions. The famous writer **Giovanni Boccaccio** (*circa* 1313 – 1375) referred to Giotto as 'the best painter in the world'. But the highest recognition came from **Dante Alighieri** (1265 – 1321) who, in his work the *Divine Comedy* called Giotto 'the master of his master' – that is to say, superior to Cimabue, who, until that time, had been regarded as the finest artist ever.

Dante and Giotto before the Italian nobleman Guido da Ravenna

Watching the sheep

Madonna on the Throne by Cimabue

As far as we know, the artistic development of the young Giotto began in the studio of the famous **Cimabue**. According to legend, the meeting between the two happened quite by chance, whilst Cimabue was crossing a field in Mugello. At the side of the path the artist saw a boy intent on drawing and so Cimabue went up to him. With great surprise he saw that the boy, dressed as a humble peasant, had drawn a sheep with remarkable ability. Astounded by such natural talent, Cimabue made up his mind to take little Giotto with him as his student.

The Expiatory Chapel

Flight into Egypt by Giotto

One of the most successful series of pictures by Giotto was done by the artist with the help of his best assistants, on the walls of the Scrovegni Chapel at Padua – a series of panels depicting the story of Christ and the Virgin Mary and a huge fresco of the Last Judgement. The work for the Scrovegni Chapel was paid for by the banker **Enrico Scrovegni**, because the honour of his family had been damaged by the behaviour of his father who had been accused of being a dishonest money-lender. As a tribute to Enrico Scrovegni, Giotto painted him in the picture showing repentance by kneeling before the Madonna and holding out to her a model of the chapel.

The far-sighted artist and inventor, a genius in science, technology and creativity

LEONARDO DA VINCI

(Vinci 1452 – Amboise 1519)

The corpse had been laid out for the anatomy lesson at the hospital of Santa Maria Nuova. Leonardo guided by instructions from the doctor in charge, lifted a sharp, thin knife. Each time he carried out a dissection of a human body, he felt the same deep emotion – the sensation of presiding at a ceremony in which the whole creation of a person is revealed in all its fine detail. Holding his breath, he traced a line along the body with his knife and cut into the tissues. There, in front of his eyes appeared the perfect system of veins, bones, muscles … what he called in his mind the 'man machine', each part fitting perfectly with all the others, designed by God as part of the most wonderful creation.

Between 1507 and 1508, Leonardo da Vinci often attended **anatomy lessons** at the hospital of Santa Maria Nuova in Florence. He did this in order to learn as much as he could about the design and the workings of the human body. This intense interest arose from his enthusiasm for science and art. After having learned what he defined as 'artistic anatomy' – a basic knowledge of the skeleton and structure of the muscles – as a teenager, he had felt the need to discover more about the actual structure of a human body in order to reproduce it as accurately as he could in his own paintings.

Leonardo was the son of a rich nobleman of Vinci (a small village in Tuscany). For him, art and science were two aspects of one whole, great project – the knowledge of a human body. Leonardo da Vinci began his artistic apprenticeship in the studio of the famous painter and sculptor **Andrea de Verrochio** in 1469. Here he found a rich source of ideas and inspiration. As well as studying sculpture and painting altarpieces, he also learned to make breastplates for armour, using tools for working in different metals.

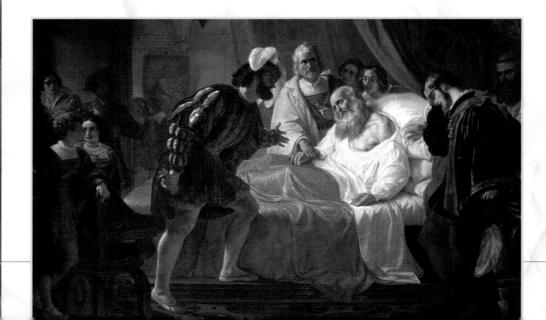

Left, *The Death of Leonardo*

The Virgin Mary, the Christ Child and Saint Anne

On the basis of technical knowledge he acquired during this time, Leonardo offered his services to the Duke of Milan, **Ludovic il Moro** in 1483. At that time, Milan was under constant threat of invasion, and Leonardo knew that the Duke wanted new **war machines**. But, soon after he arrived at Ludovic's court at **Sforzesca**, Leonardo found that they were more enthusiastic about his talents as an artist, rather than his scientific ability and mechanical experience. Excluded from academic circles because of his poor knowledge of Latin (the reason why he was defined at this time as 'a man without letters') Leonardo filled most of the gaps with a self-taught education.

In 1500, Milan was invaded by the troops of the French king **Louis XII** and Ludovic il Moro was defeated. So, Leonardo returned to Florence. In 1502, he was employed by **Cesare Borgia**, the richest and most powerful man in the whole of Rome, as a military planner and to design war machines. After Cesare Borgia was killed in 1507, Leonardo turned once more to art, working on some of his most famous paintings, such as the Mona Lisa (*La Gioconda*) and many interpretations of the legend of Leda, beloved of the Greek Zeus and who was changed into a swan. Slowly, honours came to Leonardo from King **Francis I** of France, who appointed him as the 'first painter, engineer and architect of the king'. He gave Leonardo a huge amount of money, as well as the right to live in the **Castle of Cloux** at Amboise, where the Italian artist and scientist died in May 1519.

Batting wing, model code-name Atlantic

Born to fly

Throughout history, there have been many people who dreamed of being able to fly through the air. Most of these people were inventors – from **Daedalus**, who, according to Greek myth, made wings of feathers and wax with which his son Icarus tried to reach the Sun, to the brothers **Orville** and **Wilbur Wright**, who in 1903 built the first successful flying machine, Flyer I. Using his genius together with his quest for adventure, Leonardo da Vinci also became part of this uninterrupted chain of brave pioneers. Some of his projects on flight, drawn after studying the physical structure of birds and their methods of rising above the ground, to soar and to glide, were forerunners of the modern parachute, the delta-plane and the helicopter.

Who is the lady behind the mysterious 'La Gioconda' painting, (more popularly known as the 'Mona Lisa'), shown left? This question has divided historians and art critics for a long time. According to the most popular theory, the woman in the picture was Lisa del Gioconda, wife of a rich Venetian merchant. The strangest theory is that the face in the picture is a self-portrait of Leonardo.

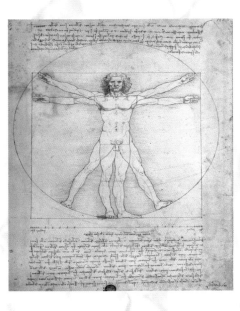

THE VITRUVIUS MAN
Developing the idea which had been put forward by the Roman architect Vitruvius (1 BC), Leonardo da Vinci defined the proportions of the human body so that this could be drawn both within a circle and within a square.

The Last Supper ...   ... restored!

Together with the 'Mona Lisa', the 'Last Supper' is probably the most famous work by Leonardo da Vinci. The fresco, painted between 1496–1498 on one wall of the refectory of the Church of Saint Mary of Grace, Milan, shows Jesus in a room with his disciples, having a Passover meal together. The picture portrays the moment when one disciple is about to betray him, Leonardo revealing the traitor by painting a fiery blade into his heart. The drama of this moment is the reason for the ragged movements and agitated expressions on the faces of the disciples, da Vinci concentrating on the reaction of some of the disciples to the words of Jesus and thus bringing to life their most heartfelt feelings of shock and dismay.

The Last Supper by Leonardo da Vinci

Before 1999, the year in which the *Last Supper* was restored, the painting was almost completely faded. The figures of Jesus and his disciples were nothing more than vague coloured shapes, with the architecture in the background almost lost in the grey of the plaster coming to the surface after hundreds of years. The reason for this deterioration is due mainly to Leonardo da Vinci. Although the dampness and the pollution of the atmosphere both contributed to the alteration in the original colouring, the technique used by him also speeded up the decay. Leonardo used a method of fresco called 'dry'. This enabled him to return more than once to the subjects he had already painted, but, unlike the classic techniques, with 'dry' fresco painting, the coloured pigments could not penetrate deeply enough into the plaster.

A 'pop' Leonardo

The *Mona Lisa* with a moustache? The figure of Christ in *The Last Supper* surrounded by fluorescent pictures? No horror pictures, or acts of vandalism – but some copies of the works of Leonardo in modern style. The first was painted in 1919 by **Marcel Duchamp** (1887–1968), an outstanding exponent of 'avant-garde' art (new ideas in art) at the beginning of the twentieth century – cubism and dadaism. Duchamp's *Mona Lisa* is a perfect reproduction – except for the moustache above the famous smile, which was painted by Duchamp to signify a break from 'traditional' art. A re-working of *The Last Supper* was painted by Andy Warhol (1928–1987), forerunner of the so-called 'pop art'. In the hands of this American artist, the central character in 'The Last Supper' becomes part of a sort of advertising poster.

La Joconde by Duchamp   *The Last Supper* by Warhol   part of *The Last Supper* by da Vinci

Left-handed mirror writing

Mirror writing is writing from right to left (in the western world, writing is done from left to right), and this is the handwriting used by Leonardo in his manuscripts. To read mirror writing, it is necessary to use a mirror. It has been believed for a long time that Leonardo adopted this system of writing to make it less easy to be read by other people. But some historians have suggested that da Vinci might have been dyslexic – a disorder which causes difficulties in reading and mistakes in writing, and with letters often written back to front and/or not in the correct order.

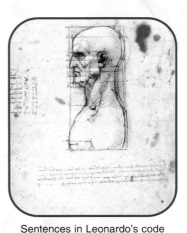

Sentences in Leonardo's code

Vegetarian

In the fifteenth century, most people were strictly vegetarian. Meat was a luxury which only the wealthy could afford. But Leonardo was not vegetarian because of any shortage of money. He did not eat meat due to his deep love of nature, and animals in particular.

The artist who combined art with the development of engraving and print-making techniques

ALBRECHT DÜRER

(Nürnberg 1471 – 1528)

The road snaked its way through the valley of the River Inn. The sky was covered with bright clouds, with only thin rays of sunlight filtering through. The carriage slowly bumped its way along, as the young man inside looked all around him, longing to reach warm, sunny Italian countryside. Cold, dismal Nürnberg was now behind him, as well as his work as an engraver and his family home, where he had also left a young wife whom he had married but did not love. With each bend in the road, it seemed to bring him closer to Venice, the end of his long journey. It would take him many days, but his heart already belonged to the Italian city, where he would begin a new chapter in his life, as an artist.

Compared to his native Nürnberg, a city of skilled workers, Venice must have appeared a completely new world in the eyes of Albrecht Dürer. The whole city was a place of culture, where different artistic styles came together and where artists were highly regarded. So it is not surprising that the time Dürer spent in Italy between 1494 and 1495 left a lasting impression on the future development of the young German artist. His never-ending search for different ideas and inspiration, both as an artist and as a person had been a particular feature of his personality since boyhood. At first, it seemed he would follow the **family tradition of being a goldsmith** by becoming an apprentice in his father's business, but he gave this up to become a painter. He became an apprentice to **Michael Wohlgemuth**, who, as well as being a fine painter, was also highly skilled as a woodcut illustrator – engraving pictures in wood blocks to be used in printing. From him, Dürer learned this skill and within a short space of time he had become a celebrated

illustrator of printed books. Dürer also gained a wide experience in the field of graphics (printing techniques) during the course of a long journey which he made through various German cities such as Cologne, Colmar and Basilea, between 1490 and 1494, working the whole time. In different studios, he learned many engraving techniques and developed a remarkable flair for using different materials. He had to return to

The Feast of the Rose Garlands by Dürer

Christ with his Cross by Dürer

The Knight, Death and the Devil by Dürer

Nürnberg in order to marry a woman chosen for him by his father, but he left soon after for Venice.

Dürer stayed only a short time in Italy before returning to Nürnberg once again. Here he became the leading artist in graphic (print-making) arts, as shown by his famous series of xylographs (engraving on wood) on the themes of the *Apocalypse* and the *Passion of the Cross*. Whilst becoming successful as an illustrator, Dürer continued to develop his passion for painting, often painting portraits and some of the most famous subjects painted by famous Italian artists, such as *The Adoration of the Magi* in 1540. But what was still lacking from his pictures was the right calculation of **perspective** – the depth and distance in a painting. To correct this gap, he undertook a second journey to Italy in 1505, where he painted *The Feast of the Rose Garlands* for the funeral chapel of the German community in the church of Saint Bartholomew, Venice. During the last part of his life, Dürer continued to divide himself between two professions – that of the engraver and the painter. He also devoted more time to studies on the human body, and the development of fortification of Venice in the event of war.

A Good Businessman

Dürer was a very generous man, often giving works of art which had taken him a great deal of time to complete in exchange for small gestures of friendship. But with this generous spirit, he was also an excellent businessman. He was one of the first artists to see that own rights were recognized and rewarded on prints made from the engravings which he did, and became both illustrator and editor when his book on the Acropolis was published.

The Agony of the Ten Thousand by Dürer

The Workman

In 1500 Dürer painted a self-portrait, which many thought was scandalous. He painted himself as **'Christ, Saviour of the World'** facing the viewer with a fixed look and his hand raised in a gesture as if he were giving a blessing. After that, he often added his own face in the background detail of a painting to signify his own role in the creation of the picture. During the Middle Ages, an artist was seen simply as a workman, but Dürer believed himself to be a true 'creator'. In the inscription behind and to the

left of his face, we can detect the words from the book of Genesis in The Bible, at the moment of the creation of the first man, Adam. 'I, Albrecht Dürer, have created myself in my own image with colours to last an eternity.'

Engravings ...

Growing up in his father's workshop, Dürer learned from boyhood numerous techniques for working with metals. His experience of using tools to make jewellery proved extremely useful later on, when he began working in xylography – book illustrations made by engravings on tablets of wood. To become an illustrator it was usually enough to be able to draw, because woodworkers normally engraved along the lines of the drawing to make it ready for printing. But Dürer always wanted perfection. To get this, he had to learn how to chisel the wood to get the effects that he wanted. The results were astounding. To illustrations in plain black and white, he added many different effects in various shades and depths of grey.

Melencolia I, copperplate engraving by Dürer

Left:
Adoration of the Christ Child, and part of *Adoration of the Magi* by Dürer

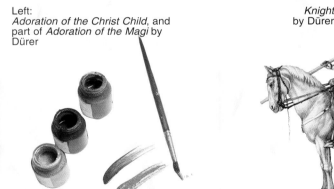

Knight by Dürer

And there was more!

As well as working with the 'drypoint' technique, where the illustration is engraved directly into copperplate with a sharp point, Dürer also obtained perfect results by using aqua forte (nitric acid) in a procedure to 'fix' a drawing on layers of copper. Artists who were searching for new techniques were enthusiastic about this development. Although **oil colours** on wood, or tempera (colours thickened with egg yolk) on cloth were more widely used, Dürer also painted in water colours, where the colours are dissolved in water so that the effect is softer and colours paler. Thirty years after he painted his first self-portrait, he became an expert in the technique of silvering. This needed the undivided attention of the artist, because there was no chance of correcting any mistakes once a mark had been made or a line drawn.

Corner of a Meadow by Dürer

To protect a name

Today, nobody can use a trademark without being prosecuted and fined for plagiarism (unauthorized copying). In the same way, all works by songwriters, composers, authors and scriptwriters and artists are protected by the laws of **copyright**, meaning the rights of the author. This law was introduced only in the twentieth century. During the time in which Dürer was living in the fifteenth century, there was nothing to protect the artist from other people copying his work. Despite this, in 1506, Dürer decided to bring before a magistrate the Bolognese engraver Marcantonio Raimondi, who had not only reproduced the illustrations of the *Life of the Virgin Mary* which Dürer had painted, but had also copied Dürer's stamp 'AD' with which Dürer had always signed his own work.

Adoration of the Magi by Dürer

Above, *Portrait of a Young Venetian Woman* by Dürer

From the brush to the pen

As well as memories of his life, which he published with the title *Family Chronicles* (1524) Dürer also wrote other papers – *On Perspective and Geometry* (1525); *On the fortification of the cities, castles and villages* (1527); *On the Proportions of the Human Body* (issued a few months after the death of the artist in 1528).

Below, left *Madonna and Child*; Below, right, *The Trinity*, both by Dürer

The sculptor who entered into legend with his painting on the ceiling of the Sistine Chapel

MICHELANGELO
(Caprese 1475 – Rome 1564)

For hours, Michelangelo had walked nervously past the room. He did not know what to do – and doing nothing was making him impatient. The marble had not arrived, and he was tired of waiting. For the whole morning, he had made sketches, composed sonnets, made notes and taken measurements. Now he wanted to begin work on his sculpture, to start chiselling at the stone to create a statue. He took a deep breath and knocked at the door. 'Who is there?' came the reply. Michelangelo's courage failed him. He ran outside into the courtyard, his heart pounding like a drum. Suddenly he slipped and fell. As he tried to get to his feet, he found he was kneeling in front of an enormous slab of white marble. At last, he managed to stand up. He paused and then he went around the marble many times, stroking its surface. An image was already forming in his mind – a Pietà, a statue of the Virgin Mary, mourning over the body of her dead son.

Presentation of his projects for the Basilica of Saint Peter

For the whole of his long life, Michelangelo Buonarroti regarded himself as a sculptor. Even though he was a skilled architect, an outstanding painter and an excellent poet, it was his sculpture which made him a legend and which lifted him above the other artists of his time. His artistic apprenticeship began in the studio of **Domenico Ghirlandaio** in 1487 and then developed in the gardens of Saint Mark in Florence, where he was able to study and to learn to make copies of statues from ancient times.

Basilica of Saint Peter

Then, just as his artistic career was developing, he suffered a serious setback because of the death of **Lorenzo de' Medici** (Lorenzo the Magnificent) in 1492. Lorenzo was a rich and powerful man who had financed Michelangelo's art and career. He was also ruler of Florence, and on his death there were many who believed that Florence should be a free state. By 1494, the de' Medici family had

Raphael and Michelangelo talking together in the Vatican

been overthrown and Michaelangelc had to leave Florence. After living in Bologna, Michelangelo returned to Florence for a short time and then in 1496, he went to Rome. Here he created his first masterpiece, the *Pietà Vaticana* (1498). By the beginning of the 1500s, he was again dividing his time between Florence and Rome. These were the years in which he created two of his most famous works – the statue of *David* (1504) to celebrate the founding of the republic of Florence, and the frescos on the ceiling of the Sistine Chapel (1508–1512) on the command of **Pope Julius II**. At the end of this important time, Michelangelo received a commission from the new **Pope Leo X** to design both the architecture and a sculpture for the new sacristy in the Church of Saint Lorenzo in Florence. Now Michelangelo could return to sculpture as well as showing his skill as an architect. At the siege of Florence in 1529, he also showed that, like Leonardo da Vinci, he was an excellent military planner, giving valuable advice on how to improve the system of defences in the city. The fall of Florence in 1530 had a deep and a lasting impression on Michelangelo. In 1534, he took the decision to leave his beloved city and go to Rome for good, where from 1536 to 1541 he painted the fresco of the *Last Judgement* in the Sistine Chapel. In his last years, he abandoned painting and sculpture completely (except for some rough sketches of *Pietà*) and devoted himself to architecture, setting out a grand project for the dome of the Basilica of Saint Peter.

David by Michelangelo

The Sibyl of Delphi on the ceiling of the Sistine Chapel

The Condemnation of Justice

During the mid 1500s, there was a lot of corruption and dishonesty within the Catholic church. In order to try and stop this, a special **Council** met between 1545 to 1563 at Trenta to make reforms. But the laws which this Council laid down led to a terrible persecution of all those who seemed not to respect religious beliefs. This persecution also applied to works of art, in particular, nude figures which were considered immoral. And so in 1564, the figures painted by Michelangelo in ***The Last Judgement*** in the Sistine Chapel were 'dressed'. This work was done by the artist **Daniele da Volterra**, who, because of this work, was later nicknamed the 'Braghettone', because he used 'braghe' (Italian word for shorts) to cover Michelangelo's original unclothed figures.

*The **Rondanini Pietà** was Michelangelo's last unfinished work – as shown by the fact that the right arm of Jesus is still in its rough state.*

*The **Pietà Vaticana** was in a strip which slants across the figure of Mary sculpted from one solid block of marble, and bears the words **Michaelangelus Bonarotus Florentinus faciebat** (sculpted by Michelangelo Buonarroti of Florence).*

*Disappointed by the result of his work, Michelangelo hit the **Pietà Bandini** with a hammer. Despite the attempt by a student to repair the statue, the signs left by the fury of the sculptor are still there: the arm of Christ is badly stuck back on and there is a total absence of his left leg.*

*Michelangelo's **Rondanini Pietà** in its rough state, (left) was centuries ahead of its time. In fact, it anticipates the twentieth century avant-garde, such as the work entitled **Man with Guitar** by the Russian sculptor **Ossip Zadkines**.*

The Madonna and the dead Christ

The theme of the Pietà was depicted by Michelangelo in many of his sculptures. Until the last days of his life he was always seeking perfection in recreating in marble the sad figure of the dead body of Christ in the arms of the Madonna. In neither the **Pietà Bandini** which he vandalized in a fit of rage, nor the **Pietà Rondanini**, which remained unfinished at his death, did he find again the inspiration which he had felt in sculpting the complex statue of the Pietà Vaticana a little more than twenty years before, and the only one of his works to be signed by him. This statue was strongly criticized by the public, mostly because Michelangelo made the Madonna appear much younger than her son, whose head is on her lap. This was not a mistake by Michelangelo, but the way he saw the Virgin Mary, an interpretation which is also present in the *Divine Comedy* by the poet **Dante Alighieri** where the Madonna is referred to as 'daughter of her son' and which is the meaning Michelangelo meant to convey. According to the Roman Catholic religion, Mary is both the mother and the daughter of Christ, because she was created by God.

Pietà by Michelangelo (part)

A dumb statue

According to legend, Michelangelo was pleased with his statue of Moses. He was dumbfounded when a person asked, 'So, why doesn't he speak?'

Painter by chance

Michelangelo maintained that sculpture was the finest form of artistic expression. And so he was not really pleased to accept the commission to paint **the ceiling of the Sistine Chapel**. Even though he knew that this undertaking would add to his reputation, he preferred to continue work on the statues of the monumental tomb of **Pope Julius II** rather than begin painting. But despite his hesitation at the beginning, he was soon completely absorbed by the task of painting a complete religious cycle in fresco, refusing the help of any assistants and preferring to do the work completely alone. It was this work which he had at first loathed which gave him the prime place in the history of art.

MICHELANGELO AND THE CINEMA

*In the film **The Agony and the Ecstacy** the American actor Charlton Heston gave a superb performance as the controversial and solitary genius of Michelangelo. One of the most famous scenes is when he turns angrily against Pope Julius II, magnificently played by Rex Harrison.*

'The art of removal'

Michelangelo believed that a statue was already inside the block of marble. According to him, the artist had only to 'set it free', chipping away all the marble which was not needed. His sculptures were created by what he called the **'art of removal'** as expressed in some of his verses:

*Nor has the finest artist any concept
That marble itself does not contain within its surplus.*

Bearded Slave by Michelangelo

Manuscript with a poem by Michelangelo

The artist who portrayed the ideals of perfect humanity with the grace and beauty of his paintings

RAPHAEL
(Urbino 1483 – Rome 1520)

For hours, the artist had been trying to complete the image of the Madonna. The drawing was well done, but the colours were not quite right. Now, he was resting for a short time before it became dark. To him it seemed that yet another day had been wasted for ever. As he put away his tools, he glanced out and happened to see a woman who was sitting in a corner near a window. The warm, soft light of twilight caressed her face,

making it glow softly along the curves of her cheeks and chin. To him, the dying rays of the Sun made the young woman look just like the image of the Virgin Mary that he could see in his mind. Inspired by this vision, Raphael took up his brushes and started painting again.

Urbino, the town in central Italy where Raphael Sanzio was born was the home of many famous artists. Raphael's father, **Giovanni Santi**, was one of these artists, highly regarded at the court of Montefeltro of Urbino, and it was in his studio that the young Raphael first learned to paint. Raphael was only 11 years old when his father died, and not long afterwards he went to Perugia to work for the famous artist **Pietro Perugino** as an apprentice. In 1500, the year in which he could call himself a 'master' for the first time, he inherited his father's business, but he soon left the care of the family studio and workshop to some of his father's workers, whilst he journeyed to Italian cities such as Siena, Orvieto and Rome to learn more about art and to develop his own style.

His artistic career really began in 1504 when he arrived in Florence, then the home of Italian renaissance (meaning re-birth). Here he painted some of his most famous masterpieces, such as *Sposalizio della Virgine*, (The Wedding) *La Bella Giardiniera*, (The Beautiful Lady Gardener) and the *Ritratto di Agnolo Doni*, (Portrait of Agnolo Doni). In 1508, at the invitation of Pope Julius II, Raphael left Florence for

Rome. Here, in competition with the talented and older Michelangelo, Raphael undertook incredibly ambitious projects, such as the fresco paintings in the **Stanza della Segnatura**, a room in the Vatican papal apartments. In the last part of Raphael's short life (he died due to an unknown illness at only thirty seven years of age), the new **Pope Leo X** offered him important commissions – such as the architecture for the building of Saint Peters and the conservatoire of ancient Rome.

Above, left: *Madonna della seggiola* ('Madonna of the Chair') by Raphael: Below, right: *Delivery of the Keys* by Perugino

Knight on horseback by Millais

The Pre-Raphaelite Brotherhood

Even before his premature death, Raphael had become a major influence in the artistic world. For centuries afterwards, his style influenced entire generations of artists who tried to imitate Raphael. In 1848, English poet and painter Dante Gabriel Rossetti, and artists William Holman Hunt and John Everett Millais founded the **Pre-Raphaelite Brotherhood**, setting themselves and many other artists against the works of these imitators – not Raphael himself whom they admired. Their aim was to paint in a more realistic, less artificial way, as artists before Raphael had done.

The main subjects of paintings and poetry written by the Pre-Raphaelites were mostly legends of the Middle Ages, parables of the Bible, characters from Dante's *Divine Comedy* and the tragedies of Shakespeare.

A veiled presence

The lady whom Raphael loved is known by the name of **Fornarina** (right) For some students, this term refers to the profession of her father, who was a goldsmith ('fornaio' in Italian). Others believe that her name refers to a Florentine word meaning 'loved one'. The girl came into Raphael's service as a maid, but she soon won the heart of the artist, becoming his companion and his model. As well as the famous painting which shows her with her head in an enormous turban, she was also portrayed by Raphael many times as the Madonna (probably also the famous 'Madonna of the Chair'). Other art critics believe the so-called *Velata* ('The Veiled One') shown left concealed the features of the lady goldsmith.

The business of angels!

The image of two **little angels** side by side is a very popular one throughout Europe. With their sweet faces and dreamy expressions, they are often used for advertisements, to decorate T-shirts, handbags and lots of other things. But perhaps few people know that these famous 'cupids' are part of a much larger picture painted by Raphael, the *Sistine Madonna* – so-called because Saint Sixtus is shown in the painting kneeling to one side of the Virgin Mary who is standing with the baby Jesus in her arms.

Sistine Madonna by Raphael (part)

The artist who captured people's souls in his paintings

VELASQUEZ
(Seville 1599 – Madrid 1660)

The roads to Rome thronged with merchants, pilgrims, guards, priests … Different smells rose into the air, mixing with cries, sounds and snatches of conversation. Velasquez looked around him as he made his way through the crowds. There were so many things he had to do – palaces to visit, works of art to value … Yet the excitement which spread through the alley-ways and the squares seemed to ensnare him. The visitors, the merchants and the clothes that they wore reflected so much rich colour that it seemed to hypnotize him and he longed to paint them. But he had to wait. Velasquez had come to Rome as a representative of the Spanish court, not as an artist.

Velasquez was born in Seville into a Portuguese family. He spent his boyhood in the studio of the artist Francesco Herrera, leaving him to study under the guidance of **Francesco Pacheo**, his future father-in-law. It was through Pacheo that Velasquez was introduced into the Spanish court of the young king **Philip IV** as a portrait painter in 1623. As well as religious themes and local landscapes, he often painted pictures where a Biblical episode is portrayed against a 'real life' scene (such as *Christ in the House of Martha and Mary*). But at this time, almost all his paintings were portraits of court nobles and the Spanish royal family. With these portraits, Velasquez began to be both famous and wealthy, and he was the only artist to be given the title **Knight of Santiago** (1658).

At his death in 1660, he was a rich and much respected man, a humble portrait painter whose name had entered into the history of art. Inspired by colour, light and the expressions of the people he painted, he had the gift of portraying on canvas the soul of his subjects – the servants, the clowns, maids, princes and kings.

Christ in the House of Martha and Mary by Velasquez

Among nobles and clowns

As court portrait painter, Velasquez revealed his artistic genius by depicting noble and wealthy people of high birth, especially the Spanish king and members of the royal family. But he was also interested in painting ordinary people, with a real fondness for the **dwarfs** and **deformed people**, who were often kept by rich people to amuse them as jesters. Despite his stark reproduction of their physical defects, Velasquez always shows respect and humanity for them in his paintings, and they referred to him as 'a very nice man'.

Philip IV by Velasquez

Don Diego's Dwarf by Velasquez

Rome and love

His second journey to Italy had a lasting impression on the private life of Velasquez. In Rome, the artist got to know and fell in love with a young woman, the painter **Flaminia Triva** (perhaps the girl depicted in the painting *Venus and Cupid*). They had a son, named Antonio.

Velasquez and Picasso

The paintings of Velasquez had a deep and lasting effect on another Spanish artist who lived more than two centuries later – **Pablo Picasso**. From boyhood, Picasso tried to re-create the effects of light and colour of the sixteenth century artist. He made countless reproductions of the works of Velasquez, especially the picture entitled *the Family of Philip IV*, better known as *Las Meninas* ('The Maids of Honour') of which there are about seventy copies.

A Man of Justice

In 1650, while he was in Rome, Velasquez made a decision which, for those times, was amazing; this was to give a **servant**, Juan de Pareja, his freedom. From the beginning, his relationship with this servant had been more that of master and student – rather than that of master and slave. Seeing that Juan had a particular talent for painting, Velasquez made him one of his assistants. To acknowledge the kindness Velasquez had shown him, Pareja remained in his service even when, according to law, he could consider himself to be a **free man**.

Servant by Velasquez

Las Meninas by Velasquez; in small square, *A Woman* by Picasso

> *The artist who captured states of the mind and atmospheres which were legendary*

REMBRANDT

(Leida 1606 – Amsterdam 1669)

The most successful time of his life and his happiest days had been spent in the house. Now it seemed to be little more than a desolate ruin. It was not only its four walls, but his own life which had been destroyed, once his bid at auction had been beaten by a higher price. The rich 'middle-class' had entered with their boots dirty with mud to seize his works, whilst he, who at one time had been a famous artist, could only stand by and watch, waiting until he could go in and collect a few poor rags and sticks of furniture which had not yet been taken. He could still hear the disapproving whispers of those who had gathered at the crossroads to see his final defeat. For Rembrandt, there would be no future without his art.

In 1656, after having been declared **bankrupt**, Harmenszoon Rembrandt stood by helplessly as his possessions were sold to pay his debts. Two years before, also because of debt, he had been forced to sell his own home. One of the most famous Dutch painters had become the

centre of a scandal.

Rembrandt was born at Leida in Holland in 1606 into a family of well-to-do millers. After having attended the famous Latin School and enrolling at university, he could have embarked on a career as a lawyer. Instead he preferred to take up art, achieving incredible success from the very beginning. In 1631, he decided to leave for Amsterdam, where there was a thriving artistic community. Within a short time of his arrival, he became an acclaimed **portrait painter** – not only of people on their own, but also group portraits, such as those which were commissioned by the corporation of surgeons. During this time, he also painted huge canvases depicting historical and religious subjects, as well as becoming a skilled **engraver** and **art collector**.

Until the end of the 1640s, Rembrandt had been a wealthy and much-admired artist. Then, his reputation was damaged in the eyes of the public because of some love affairs and at the same time his dramatic and intense style lost favour with his clients. Loneliness, poverty and losses clouded the final years of his life. He died alone and forgotten in 1669.

Top, left: *The Stone Bridge* by Rembrandt

The Anatomy Lesson by Rembrandt

The Night Watch by Rembrandt

Rembrandt, True and False

Despite the title which it was given in the seventeenth century, the setting of the picture *The Night Watch* was not night-time. Rembrandt used contrasts of shade, darkness and light, not to indicate that the action was taking place at night, but to create a dense atmosphere and to make the expressions of the people more intense. Instead of being simply **a group portrait**, Rembrandt makes it a piece of real life, a scene being enacted. Many misunderstandings about the life and the work of Rembrandt – such as that of *The Night Watch* – have recently been explained thanks to the **Rembrandt Research Project**, a programme instituted in 1968 with the aim of analysing the most significant episodes of Rembrandt's artistic life and bringing to light the deepest significance of his paintings.

Hendrickje Bathing by Rembrandt

Woman at her Toilet by Degas (part)

Research by the artist

Rembrandt's interest in anatomy is shown by the number of times he scrutinized his own face (over seventy self-portraits), as well as that of his wife **Saskia** (above, as the goddess Artemis), his last close companion **Hendrickje** and his son **Tito**. The purpose of these paintings (half bust or a complete figure with costumes of the time or nude) was his analysis of the facial expressions and the pose of the body. Rembrandt did not only paint his own family circle as they actually were, but used them as subjects in the huge canvasses he painted which depicted ancient legends and stories from the Bible, thus bringing the people in those stories to life with their moods and gestures.

The mysterious Hebrew world

At Amsterdam, Rembrandt lived for twenty years in a house in the Anthonisbreestraat, one of many in the **Jewish quarter**. During this time, the artist made lasting friendships with members of the Jewish community, in particular the Rabbi Menasseh ben Israël. One of the things Rembrandt learned from this man of great culture was a basic knowledge of the **cabala** – according to which there existed a code, based on letters and symbols, which could interpret the mysteries of the world. Rembrandt remained deeply fascinated by this and many art historians believe that it influenced his paintings, even to the extent of hidden signs and meanings.

The artist who brought new life to Japanese art by the extent of his creativity

HOKUSAI
(Edo, now Tokyo, 1760 – 1849)

From the first light of dawn, the studio had been filled with artists. Hokusai had been bent over a sheet of paper for more than an hour – but it seemed that no image would come. Every so often, he raised his hand and traced signs in the air, as if he were drawing an unseen picture. But the loud, almost non-stop chattering of his students made it impossible for him to concentrate. All at once he jumped to his feet and strode to the window, looking out. A girl was outside, on the sea shore. And it was then that Hokusai found the inspiration which he had been seeking for so long.

Hokusai became interested in art at the age of six. The artist himself wrote that from childhood he had felt the need to reproduce on paper 'the shape of things'. Poor and without any hope of going to art school, he had to wait many years until he could begin his artistic career. This was in 1775, when he became an apprentice to a **wood block engraver**, although this was in a print-shop and not in a studio.

After about a year, he went to the artistic studio of the famous artist and print-maker Shunsho who was well-known for his **ukiyo-e** ('pictures of the floating world'). It was from Shunsho that Hokusai learned the same technique as well as making his own prints and illustrations for books.

In 1793 Shunsho died and Hokusai decided to experiment with new methods of painting. For over thirty years, he had wanted to work independently of any other artist and it was his study of Chinese and eastern painting which helped him achieve this. Hokusai's interest in the **perspective** (depth and distance in a painting) led to his spending a great deal of time walking. This interest is shown in his paintings, where what was simply the background before becomes the main focus of his pictures. This interest also led to him creating in 1830 the astounding series *Twenty six views of the Fuji Mountain*, of

which the painting '*Breaking Wave off Kanagawa*' was one. Through this work, Hokusai became a true and much-admired master of art, whose style inspired many imitations. But still he continued to try out new ideas in painting and in print-making, constantly striving to achieve his own idea of perfection. It was only shortly before his death that he had a little time to think back over the masterpieces of his lifetime's work.

Walking in a print by Hokusai

The subject of the picture by Hokusai entitled **Breaking Wave off Kanagawa** *is not the sea or the fishing boat almost submerged in the waves, but Mount Fuji just visible in the background.*

The floating world

The **ukiyo-e** (pictures of the floating world) school of Japanese art – used in both painting and print-making – influenced Hokusai's work throughout his life. **Ukiyo-e** is a particular way of depicting a scene from real life – e.g. landscapes, women in traditional Japanese costume and the actors of **Kabuki** (traditional Japanese theatre). Leading artists of the ukiyo-e style were the artists **Kitagawa Utamoro** and **Ichiryusai Hiroshighe**, as well as Hokusai.

Rehearsal scene of the Kabuki theatre

Names for all times

At his birth, the artist known by the name of Hokusai was actually named Tokitaro. '**Taro**' because he was the first son, and '**toki**' to indicate that he had been born in the year of the **dragon** (according to the eastern calendar). But 'Hokusai' was only one of many names, each one characteristic of a particular phase of his life and artistic career.

TETSUZO 'warehouse of iron' (the period during which he had not yet begun his phase as a painter);

SHUNRO 'splendour of spring' (the beginning of his artistic apprenticeship in a famous studio in Edo);

HOKUSAI 'star of the north' (the moment at which he decided to paint in his own style). As well as these names, there were also others, such as Kasamara, Sori and Tamekazu.

Hokusai the foolish

Hokusai called himself 'the old man mad with painting'. According to numerous **legends**, it does seems to be true that he was a bit foolish, at least about his art. For instance – it is said that he delighted in putting his artistic talent to seemingly impossible limits, such as reproducing the flight of many birds on a single grain of rice. According to one story, one day, he began painting on an enormous sheet of paper in front of a curious crowd. nothing strange in that – except, instead of a paint-brush, Hokusai was using a broom!

Right, the head of a dragon; below, Manga is reviewed in a Japanese newsstand

MANGA

Between 1814 and 1819, Hokusai painted, along with helpers and assistants, ten **Manga**. *These were not, as might be thought by the name, the type of Japanese cartoon, widely known as 'manga', but books for teaching the art of drawing. The name comes from '**man**' (Japanese word for 'unintentional') and **ga** meaning 'images'.*

The artist who painted his own impressions by surrounding himself with nature

CLAUDE MONET
(Paris 1840 – Giverny 1926)

The misty eyes of the old artist, Monet, could see nothing more than blurred outlines. Away from the natural daylight of his garden, he had been trying for hours to recreate the images he could see in his mind and which for many months had guided his brush across the canvas – the delicate flowers of water-lilies reflected in a clear mirror of water. Using only his sense of touch to choose the tubes of paint that he needed, he began mixing colours on his palette. Then, before beginning work, he took a deep breath as the image came once again to his mind – a vision of pure cobalt blue, deep green, tiny points of yellow and soft reflections of pinks and blues.

The town of Giverny was the final stop in a long journey, both in real life and in the artistic career of Claude Monet. Except for a few short absences, the artist lived here from 1890 until his death. It was at Giverny that he found the peace and quiet of the simple country life which he found necessary in order to paint, and where, despite his failing sight, he painted his most famous series of works dedicated to *water-lilies*. Monet's artistic life began a short distance away at Le Havre, a small French seaside town, where his parents had moved in 1845 to open a grocer's shop. A chance encounter in 1856 with the landscape painter **Eugène Boudin** was lucky for the young Monet, who until then had been an

Gare Saint Lazare by Monet

unknown cartoonist. On the advice of Boudin, Monet went to Paris, which at that time was the undisputed centre of art, to become an apprentice and to learn to paint scenes from nature. There, in the lecture hall of the Swiss Academy, he found inspiration and ideas in the company of artists such as Camille Pissarro, who, like him, were seeking to develop a new style of painting. In 1860, Claude Monet was called up by the French Government to do military service in the army. He was sent to **Algeria** and spent some time in Africa, where he became ill. He returned to Le Havre to recuperate, but by 1862 he was in Paris once again, where he got to know fellow artists **Auguste Renoir**, **Alfred Sisley** and **Frédéric Bazille**. They rented a boarding house outside the city so that they could paint *en plain air* (in the fresh air) and it was from their experimentations with light and colour that the **Impressionist movement** developed. Poor reviews by the critics and the continual money problems forced Monet to leave Paris. After a happy time living at Argenteuil (1871 – 1878) where he often worked in close contact with his friends in the Impressionist movement, there were sad days for him at Véntheuil, with still more poverty which unfortunately contributed to the premature death of his wife Camille in 1879.

Then, Monet's luck changed with the beginning of his fame and long-awaited good fortune. No longer worried about money, he was able to buy the house and the **gardens of Giverny**. In his old age he could dedicate himself to painting and to the water-lilies.

Top right,
The Bed of Water-lilies (part);
below, *The Sisters Hoschede*
by Monet

Monet, whilst painting
on board his boat-studio
from a painting by Édouard Manet

On a boat on the river

In 1874, Claude Monet was painted by his friend, the artist **Édouard Manet**, as Monet sat painting on his boat. This was Monet's **boat-studio** which the artist had bought the year before in 1872, modifying it to make it into a proper floating studio, with plenty of space for his canvases and awnings to shelter him from the sun. During the years he spent at Argenteuil, Monet never went far from the Seine in search of inspiration and he analyzed everything reflected in the light and on the surface of the water. Later, when he had more money, he bought other boats, one of which had a cabin covered over so tightly that it could be used as a trampoline for **diving**, an activity much enjoyed by Monet during the hot summer days.

A paradise of colours

One of the ponds created by Monet in the garden of his house at Giverny

The garden at Monet's house at Giverny was a true oasis of peace. To him, it was a delightful corner of paradise with flowers of every colour and trees mirrored in water. In 1890, when Monet decided to buy it, the land was wild and overgrown. Monet made many changes in order to transform the land into a garden which would be the ideal surroundings for his paintings. This needed a lot of money, enormously hard work and many arguments with the authorities to carry out all the changes necessary for his plans. The largest part of the work was a **pond for water-lilies** which was created by partially diverting the course of the river.

Water-lilies by Monet (part)

Box of colours

Rivals and allies

1839 is officially recognized as the year when **photography** was born. The advent of this new technology had a lasting impact on the world of art. Before this, rich people had turned to painters for self-portraits. Now, almost anyone could be photographed for a more accurate picture and at a much cheaper price. It might have been thought that the mid-nineteenth century brought hard times for painters, but this was not the case. Instead, photography brought freedom for artists. Now they were not forced to paint just what they saw. Instead, they were free to paint scenes according to their particular 'impressions'. Some, like Monet, were also keen photographers and used cameras and photographic equipment to study a particular location before painting it.

Freedom of colour

Before the invention of **zinc tubes** in the mid nineteenth century, it was difficult for artists to paint in the open air. Before the artist began work, colour pigments had to be ground up and diluted with various types of oil (linseed, or corn oil, for example) to keep the colour fluid. With zinc tubes there came the possibility of acquiring the mixture ready-made, with the metal of the container keeping the paint at the right consistency before the tube was closed again to prevent waste. All this prompted artists to leave their studios, enabling them to work in direct contact with nature.

Impressionism

Impressionists

Monet, Pissarro, Degas and the other members of the impressionists group were great friends, as well as being talented artists who were well-known in the artistic world of Paris. They also shared the dream of a new style of painting, free from the bonds of traditional teaching and based on observations of life in its various forms. Although they were friends, each artist was different to the others in temperament, life-style and way of interpreting art, and so they often made decisions independent of the others.

The Dance Class. Edgar Degas *liked to paint men and women at their everyday work, such as washerwomen and milliners, both in the studio and in the open air. His favourite subjects were ballet dancers. As he became blind, he also modelled these dancers in wax.*

Monte Saint-Victoire. Paul Cézanne *painted this subject many times with the aim of putting one of his own theories to the test. Studying the effects produced by the vision on the eye, he believed that distant objects tend to assume a bluish colouring after a while.*

The Shepherdess. *During the final phase of his artistic career* **Camille Pissarro** *experimented with the technique of 'pointillism' which was introduced at the end of the nineteenth century by Georges Seurat and Paul Signac. This consisted of creating an image using only tiny points of complementary colours – for example, yellow and blue to create green.*

Breakfast on the Grass. *This painting caused a scandal when it was painted in 1863. But it was this which brought the artist,* **Édouard Manet** *to the attention of the new Impressionist group. The picture, with its sharp contrasts of bright and very dark colours, seems very different to those of his close friend, Monet.*

Rouen Cathedral *Monet painted about fifty canvasses of Rouen Cathedral to capture the different effects produced by the light on the front face of the building at different times of the day.*

The Cradle *Berthe Morisot had a real talent for painting the motherly figure.*

Impression, Sunrise. *It was this picture, painted by* **Monet** *and exhibited in 1874, which gave the Impressionists their name and so became the symbol of their 'turning away' from 'official' types of art.*

The artist who suffered from depression, yet painted so many pictures with the colours of the sun

VINCENT VAN GOGH
(Groot Zunder 1853 – Auvers-sur-Oise 1890)

On the evening of 27 July 1890, a man staggered through the fields at Auvers-sur-Oise near Paris. Injured on one side by a shot from a fire-arm, Vincent Van Gogh left behind him a trail of blood, blotting red the fiery yellow of the fields of wheat at sunset. Yet, even in this final act of despair, it was yellow and orange which dominated the scene, the colours which had been mixed and blended so many times on the artist's palette. Now, Van Gogh himself was the centre of the picture, in a field beneath the still dazzling sun, a bluish sky specked with the wings of black crows.

Vincent Van Gogh died peacefully two days after he shot himself, murmuring to his beloved brother Theo 'I have done this for the good of everyone'. Now, after a life almost entirely dedicated to art, a total passion which had pushed him to the limits of madness, only Van Gogh's paintings would remain as evidence of his never-ending quest for the meaning of life. As he wrote in a letter to his friend, the artist **Émile Bernard**, he had sought 'all that which really exists' – a solitary walk, an atmosphere of suspense, men bent over their tasks, hard at work.

Van Gogh's father was a pastor, and he himself became a preacher. In 1878, he did missionary work among the poor at Borinage, at that time a coal-mining area in Belgium. Van Gogh's experience with the people of Borinage and their surroundings deeply affected the way that he saw everything. He left Borinage in 1880, but even after he returned to the family home, then at the Dutch village of Neunen,

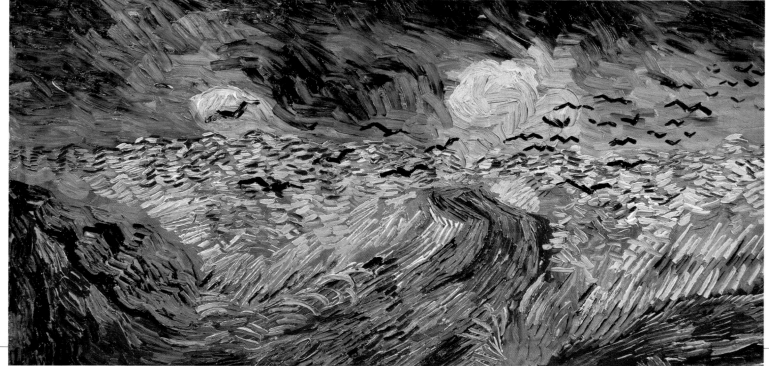

Wheat Field with Rooks, painted by Vincent Van Gogh

the influence of his time at Borinage showed in the dark and muddy colours of the pictures he painted between 1883 and 1885. Van Gogh lived in Paris for two years, from 1886 to 1888. During this time, his colours mellowed into softer and more mellow tones. Curious about the theories on the sharply contrasting colours used by **Georges Seurat** and **Camille Pissarro**, Van Gogh also tried this technique, in particular contrasting red and green, and so bringing a stronger expression to his paintings.

He then moved to Arles in southern France, where there was a thriving artistic community. Here, Van Gogh's colours almost exploded into a dazzling fire of yellow-orange rays, such as the disc of the sun at the centre of the painting *Sower at Sunset*. This area of France represented not only a new light to Van Gogh, but also a strange foreboding of his loss of sanity. A nervous breakdown led to a stay in the psychiatric hospital of Saint Rémy de Provence, and the influence of this experience, too, was shown in his work. The manager at Saint Rémy de Provence, Jean-François Poulet, reported that he had seen Van Gogh swallowing

The Scream by Edvard Munch

the contents of his tubes of paint, the same colours that he had used to cut with sharp brush-strokes on the faces of prisoners in the *Wheel of Incarceration* depicting ghostly figures walking around in a claustrophobic circle. To his sister Wilhelmina, he wrote 'in our faces today are expressions of passion, like a long wait, a cry'. That cry was Van Gogh's own which followed the echo of gunshot across a field of wheat on a summer sunset.

The Sower at Sunset by Vincent Van Gogh

Scarring his own face

Van Gogh's unending search for the meaning of life was not limited to the observation of people and nature, as shown in many of his pictures; it was a search which also compelled him to cut his own face, as a despairing attempt to get some sort of answer. From 1886 to 1890, Van Gogh painted **twenty self-portraits**. In some he appears quite normal, an elegantly-dressed man little more than thirty years old. At other times, his face is disfigured by sadness, a person looking at himself and realizing the signs of a tormented madness.

The anxiety on the face of the young woman painted in the picture entitled 'The Italian Woman' is underlined with the lashing of colour – scratches of green on the skin, used to capture the all-consuming melancholy in her eyes, lost in space.

The Van Gogh museum in Amsterdam

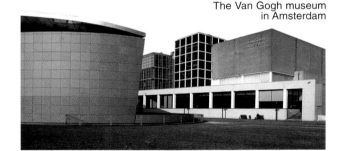

Artistic loneliness

At Arles, Van Gogh dreamed of the creation of a community of artists. The renting of a home-studio, the **yellow house**, and the arrival of his friend, **Paul Gaugin**, was meant to be the prelude of a revolutionary artistic experiment. The dream was soon broken. In December 1889, the friendship between the two artists broke down completely. Gaugin left the house, and in an act of desperation, Van Gogh cut off part of his ear. There was nobody else who could attempt to understand completely the mind and the art of Vincent Van Gogh. Apart from a few commissions and barter, the only picture which he succeeded in selling during his lifetime was *The Red Vineyard*, which was bought for 400 francs by the artist Anne Boch.

Van Gogh

Van Gogh at thirteen years old

A heavy burden of heredity

Vincent Van Gogh was deeply aware of having inherited the name of a dead brother. Throughout his life, he questioned whether he had taken the place of another individual who might have been able to live with more purpose than him. The **melancholia** (depression) from which he suffered was a trait of the Van Gogh family. Theo, the brother who backed Van Gogh financially and with whom he carried out a long correspondence (over 600 letters) died in a nursing home for the mentally ill less than six months after the death of Vincent, and his sister **Wilhelmina** remained in an institution for the mentally ill, suffering from severe depression for thirty eight years. Van Gogh's younger brother **Cornelius** also had his share of misfortune, after being wounded in battle during the Boer War (South Africa 1899 – 1902).

The Van Gogh family home at Neunen

Below, registration of Van Gogh at the academy
Right, Van Gogh's house in Paris

Vincent Van Gogh, portrait by Henri de Toulouse Lautrec

Vincent Van Gogh, from a picture by Renato Guttuso

The artist who broke up the human body and the world in a myriad of multi-formed fragments

PABLO PICASSO

(Malaga 1881 – Mougins 1973)

The day had become night once again. Picasso had slept the whole afternoon. Now it was the turn of his friend, Max, to take the bed. He began preparing to begin painting, as the sun set over Paris. He arranged the canvas on his easel and set out his paints and his brushes. Then he went to the window for a few seconds, watching the people walking about in the street. In one corner, he could see a beggar raising his hand in a plea for a few coins from the more prosperous passers-by. Picasso fixed his eyes on the old man's ragged clothes with his wrinkled face, almost destroyed by the passing of the years and with nobody to care about him. For Picasso, the beggar was another person to add to his gallery of people whom he would paint in different shades of blue, the colours of the sky and of suffering.

In 1902, Spanish artist Pablo Picasso, moved into the poor Paris home of his friend, the writer **Max Jacob**. Although he would have to sleep by day and paint by night, because there was only one bed, it was during this time that Picasso painted some of his most intense and successful pictures. These paintings, depicting solitude and characterized by the colour blue, were prompted by the suicide of his friend Carlos Casagemas in 1901. For Picasso, his sad death marked the beginning of a new phase in his artistic career.

After leaving Spain and a formal art education, in Paris he found an environment rich in ideas and giving him the inspiration which he needed. His first few years in the French capital were difficult and he was always very short of money. Yet, this time proved to be very valuable in the development of his future experimentation in art. After having studied the human figure (first, in

acrobats, which he painted in soft tones of red, and then similar images of **African men** in the picture *Les Demoiselles d'Avignon*) Picasso began a completely new method of art. Around 1909, working with the French artist **Georges Braque**, he started **Cubism**, an artistic movement which became famous in a very short time. The success of Cubism did not stop Picasso continuing to experiment with new ideas and techniques, not only for paintings but also collages (works composed of different materials). He also created sculptures and designed sets for the theatre.

In addition, he soon became skilled as an engraver and from 1946, he began working in **ceramics** (working in clay) whilst

Les Demoiselles d'Avignon by Pablo Picasso

Le Havre by Pablo Picasso

still continuing to develop new methods of painting. For a short time, he painted in a more classical style, followed by visionary themes, similar to those of Surrealism which focused on sleep and dreams.

Pablo Picasso became the undisputed leader of art in the twentieth century and the only artist of the 'avant garde' who is known to have continually renewed his own style. He died in 1973 at the age of ninety two years. From the first acrobats to the **deformed faces** of his final period, from the statue made of soft wires to the dramatic pictures of war, Picasso widened the field of modern art more than any other artist, and inspired artists of future generations.

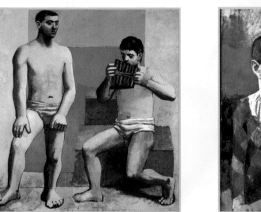

Picasso, period by period

Picasso's search for new subjects and new methods of art was varied and rather disjointed. Works of experimentation were often followed by sudden re-thinking and a return to solutions which he had set out before. But despite all this, it is possible to identify some phases of his work.

THE BLUE PERIOD (1901) – so-called because of the dominating cold colours, in particular blue and azure. Subjects painted at this time belonged to the world of the hopeless – the tramps, the old and deserted and the beggars.

THE PINK PERIOD (1905) takes its name from the pale pink and rose tints which Picasso used at the end of his Blue Period. But the different colours on the faces of acrobats and clowns continued to highlight a note of sad melancholy.

THE CUBIST PERIOD (1909) is divided between the so-called 'analytic' phase, where the figures (men, and, more often, still life) are broken up into lots of cubes, almost totally greyish, and characterized by the return of some colour, plus the use of different materials in one work – the famous Picasso collages.

THE NEO-CLASSICAL PERIOD (the 1920s) characterized by a renewed interest in the human body shape.

THE SURREALIST PERIOD (the 1930s) where the shape of objects and people, deformed and distorted, assume strange-looking shapes and unreal forms.

From the top, clockwise, *The Pipes of Pan, Acrobat and the Young Clown; The Acrobat's Wife; Portrait of Ambroise Vollard*

147

An American in Paris

At the beginning of the twentieth century, Picasso was part of the group of artists and writers who met in the apartment of American brother and sister **Gertrude** and **Leo Stein** in the rue de Fleurus in Paris. The central figure was Gertrude, a friendly and unconventional woman, who would understand and promote some of the most groundbreaking movements of 'avant-garde' – such as the expressionism of the *fauves* (French word meaning 'wild beasts', of which the chief exponent was the artist **Henri Matisse**), and the Cubism of **Georges Braque** and Pablo Picasso. Her interests were not limited to the world of art, but also extended to literature. A talented writer herself, she gave useful advice to novelists whom she defined as '**the lost generation**', including **Francis Scott Fitzgerald** and **Ernest Hemingway**.

Gertrude Stein

The artist and the theatre

A feature of the artistic career of Picasso was continual experimentation with techniques and different styles – not only with paintings, but also with sculptures and engravings. His never-ending search for different ways of expressing creative art prompted his friend, the writer Jean Cocteau, to offer him work as a set designer for the **Russian Djagilev Ballet Company**. His relationship with the theatre which began with the painting of the stage curtain and the scenery for the musical *Parade*, led to the creation of astounding sets and spectacular costumes for numerous theatrical productions, such as *The Three-Cornered Hat* and *The Four Faces of Punch*.

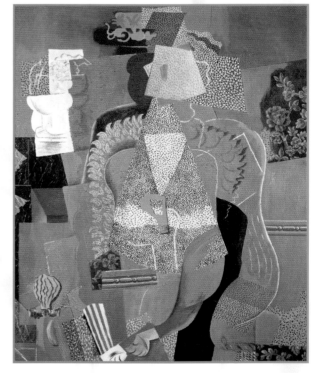

Fascinating fact

It is amazing to think that Picasso was actually born dead. According to family legend, it is said that he gave no sign of life at birth. His mother said that he was '**brought back to life**' thanks to an uncle who was a doctor and who saw that his nephew was alive and and blew cigar smoke in his nose to stimulate his breathing.

Still Life by Pablo Picasso

Above, right: *Portrait of a Clown*

Under accusation

In 1911, Picasso and his friend, the poet **Guillaume Apollinaire** were involved in a court case which created a scandal – the **theft** of the painting the *Mona Lisa* by **Leonardo da Vinci** from the Louvre Museum in Paris.

It happened because Picasso was fascinated at that time by primitive art and he had bought some antique statuettes from an acquaintance of Apollinaire by the name of Gary-Pierot. In fact, Picasso and Apollinaire were unaware that these statuettes had been stolen. As a known thief, Gary-Pierot was questioned about the disappearance of the *Mona Lisa*, and so Apollinaire and Picasso were also implicated. Both were questioned at length and they even had to spend a short time in prison, before the truth was established and the guilty culprit found – the Italian immigrant Vincenzo Perugia.

*Portrait of Apollinaire
by Giorgio de Chirico*

From 1946, Picasso also worked in clay. By that time he had made his home at Vallauris in southern France, where he installed a kiln and all the tools that he needed.

In the film **Surviving Picasso** the American director James Ivory tried to portray the complex, many-sided personality of Pablo Picasso. In particular, he concentrated on the relationships between the artist and the women whom he had loved.

*Guernica is the name of a Basque town destroyed on 26 April 1937 by German bombing during the Spanish Civil War. A few months after this tragic event, Picasso painted **Guernica**, an enormous painting (about three metres high and eight metres long) as a dramatic appeal for peace.*

*The artist who transformed suffering
in her symbolic and visionary paintings*

FRIDA KAHLO

(Coyoacán 1907 – 1954)

*The bus rattled along the crowded street of Mexico City. Frida Kahlo
looked up from the book on her knees, glancing out of the window. The
day had been long and tiring. Now it was time to have a rest. It was nice
to be returning home. For a moment, her eyes closed with tiredness.
Later, she remembered thinking that something was happening.
Suddenly, she was thrown into a whirl of bodies and steel, rolling around helplessly inside the bus,
feeling sick and frightened. Before losing consciousness, she realized in her confusion that she had
been involved in a serious road traffic accident.*

On 17 September 1925, Frida Kahlo was involved in a terrible road traffic accident. As a result,
she had to spend almost four months in bed. During this time, she made a decision to fight her
suffering through painting, an activity which was to become the main focus of her short life.
Born and brought up in Coyoacán, a suburb of Mexico City, she learned her basic art from her
father, who was a photographer, and then whilst waiting to
begin at the preparatory school for the **Faculty of
Medicine**, in the studio of an advertisement designer.

Melting Gold by Diego Rivera

Painting was only a leisure pastime, but after the tragic
event of 1925, it became her reason for living. Her
marriage to **Diego Rivera**, a famous painter of murals,
helped to further her career and she established a
reputation as a fine artist. Frida and her husband put their
works on show in an exhibition at New York in 1938 and
in Paris in 1939, which brought her worldwide fame. As
well as the approval of art critics, she was given important
appointments, such as lecturer at the academy of art *La
Esmeralda* (Mexico City). In her final years, despite
numerous medical examinations and stays in hospital for
treatment on her leg and spine, which had never
completely healed after the road accident, Frida Kahlo
continued painting with determination. As well as painting
pictures, she dedicated herself to **politics**, and in 1928 she was enrolled into the Mexican
Communist Party. Above all, she did all that she could for the promotion of world peace and for
the cultural integration of Mexican ethnic minorities.

The two Fridas by Frida Kahlo

A tortured body

The artistic career of Frida Kahlo was completely overshadowed by sadness. Her paintings often depicted bloody hearts, cut-up bodies, **symbols of death** … But this was not because of a liking for gruesome subjects, but an attempt to try and re-construct in artistic form the **tragedy** which had struck her in 1925. One day in September, whilst coming home from school, the bus in which she was travelling collided with a tram. Frida managed to save herself, but her feet and spine were seriously injured. From that moment, pain and suffering became part of her existence – a continual succession of stays in hospital and countless operations, symbolized in the tiniest details of her dramatic pictures.

The Mexico of Frida

Frida Kahlo deeply loved Mexico, the country of her birth. She was proud of her **origins** (German and Indian), and in her pictures she painted many of the traditional symbols of Mexican culture, as well as those of the Mayan and Aztec civilizations, and of European and Christian extraction. This last feature is evident above all in her **ex voto** composition – painted tablets, which are often seen in churches and chapels as a token of thanks for a cure or for escaping danger.

The Autobus by Frida Kahlo

Highs and lows of a love

The human and artistic fortunes of Frida Kahlo were closely tied to that of the artist **Diego Rivera**. Both Mexican, they shared a love of their nation and their art. Their lives were linked for the first time in 1922, when Diego Rivera was appointed to paint a mural in the school where Frida was preparing to enter the University of Medicine. When Frida began to paint following her accident, Diego became her guide, her advisor and also her companion. Their **wedding** in 1929 was the start of a partnership which lasted until Frida's death – and succeeded in overcoming betrayal, separations and even a divorce.

The Growing of Corn by Rivera

Frida Kahlo's studio

In Memory

The spirit of Frida Kahlo is kept in the '**blue house**' at Coyoacán – her paintings, her furniture which she chose and used, her jewels and clothes in which she dressed for numerous self-portraits, the garden she loved so much and her ashes, in one of her vases in the Pre-Columbian style. In the rooms of this **museum-house**, given to Mexico by Frida's husband and opened to the public in 1958, the magic which gave life to her visionary and fantastic world continues to live, immortalized in the pictures of Frida Kahlo.

The painter of light and shade who lived among obscure alley-ways and sumptuous palaces

Michelangelo Merisi, known as
CARAVAGGIO
(Caravaggio 1571 – Porto Ercole 1610)

Knight of Malta by Caravaggio

Michelangelo Merisi, better known as Caravaggio, was able to capture both the drama and the soul of a person by painting the **eyes with light and shade**. In 1610, he died alone on a beach at Porto Ercole.

Arriving in Rome from his native Caravaggio (a district near Milan) around 1592, he perfected his own art in the most degraded quarters of the Papal city, where for years he painted the suffering of the lowest classes of humanity. Later on, these people would be part of canvasses commissioned by Italian nobles and Popes – not as tramps and beggars, but in the form of the Madonna and the saints, uplifted just as he had been when he entered the palaces of the nobles.

Arrested many times for petty crimes, in 1606 he committed a **murder**. Despite being able to boast influential friends and being a famous artist, he had to flee from Rome.

He was given a hiding place by the noble family of Colonna in Milan, and then travelled to Naples and on to Malta in 1607. Here his arrival was celebrated as a visit by a famous artist, and he was even received into the Order of Malta as a **Knight of Justice**. However, when the news of his crimes reached the island he had to escape. He returned to Italy, fleeing from one city to another. His plan was to reach Rome and obtain a pardon from the Pope. This the Pope granted, but only when Caravaggio had already died as mysteriously as he had lived.

Head of Medusa by Caravaggio

Road of Life

Lurid drinking places, inns of ill repute, gaming houses frequented by thieves and assassins, squalid bordellos … this was the environment in which the artistic genius of Caravaggio developed – a Rome hidden in the shadows, tolerated and sometimes secretly encouraged by the Papal court, and where the young artist found models and inspiration. Centuries after, in the twentieth century, another Italian artist, the writer and film director **Pier Paolo Pasolini** (1922 – 1975) vividly described in his 1955 novel *Ragazzi di vita* ('Children of Life') the seventeenth century squalor of the Rome suburbs, where Caravaggio was born, where he grew up and where he died.

Pier Paolo Pasolini

WRITERS
POETS
and
PLAYWRIGHTS

The greatest poet who ever lived?
Or an anonymous story-teller?

HOMER
(circa 12th – 13th Centuries BC)

In the 'agora' – the main meeting place in the cities of ancient Greece – there was a festive atmosphere. Children played and ran about among the grown-ups, whilst old people chatted, sitting in the shade of the buildings. Suddenly, there appeared an old man, limping along with the aid of a knobbly stick. One or two people pointed to him, signalling to those around them to be quiet and to bow, almost as if they were in the presence of a god. Silently and with great respect, the people made their way to the centre of the agora, watching the old man take his place. A moment's pause, and then he began to speak, his voice ringing out, his mouth trembling with emotion. Stories of warlike rages, fearless heroes, bloody duels, impossible undertakings and loyal friendship resounded into the air.

In ancient times, stories became widely known through an **aoidos**, meaning 'singer'. We would call such a person a **bard**, or poet – someone who would journey from one place to another, telling stories from memory, tales where history and mythology were woven together in the form of **epics**. In time, these stories were written down, laying the foundations for epic poems. Between legend and real life, between the world of the story-teller and the writer, we find Homer. Whether he was a man who actually lived or an imaginary person, he was the first to have been called a poet. Homer has fascinated all kinds of people for centuries, because the works bearing his name and which originated at a time of ancient culture were the birth of western classical literature. From this ghostly aoidos came the two most famous of all epic poems, *The Iliad* and *The Odyssey. The Iliad* is about the Trojan War – in fact Homer had not yet been born at the start of this war in 1260 BC. It is believed that he came from Chios or Smyrna and that he was **blind**.

A Poor Sappho, painted by Vincenzo Busciolano

A modern odyssey

In 1922, the Irish novelist **James Joyce** (left, shown in a painting) wrote a novel entitled *Ulysses* – a modern version of Homer's *Odyssey*: but, whereas Homer's story tells of the mythical and unending voyage of the Greek hero Ulysses, Joyce made his hero a twentieth century man. Joyce's *Ulysses* begins on 16 June 1904 when a man called Leopold Bloom leaves his apartment and begins a strange and difficult journey through the streets of Dublin, Eire. During the course of Bloom's 'odyssey', he has to face many obstacles, and meet many types of people, from an impoverished tramp to the headmistress of a school, each character seeming to make Bloom's journey longer and take him further away from his destination – the house where his faithful wife Molly is waiting for him.

A question about Homer

For centuries, students of Greek literature have argued over a question about Homer and his works. How was it possible, some ask, that the same author could have written two books which were so different as *The Iliad* and *The Odyssey*? Some people believe that these poems must have been the work of more than one person, after comparing different parts in the two poems where there are clear changes in style, language and content. Literary critics are basically divided into two groups – those who say that Homer was the author of the two works (with *The Iliad* composed in his youth and *The Odyssey* in his later years) and those who believe that the two poems were the results of stories collected and re-told over the centuries by many different story-tellers and which were originally passed on by word of mouth.

Scene from *The Iliad* on a vase

A city which vanished, then came to light

The Iliad is an epic poem by Homer about the war between the Greeks and the Trojans. The city of Troy was protected all around by an immensely strong **wall**. On the other side of this wall, not only the bloodiest of battles were fought, but also the fiercest duels, such as the one between the heroes of Greek legend, Achilles and the Trojan Prince Hector. Troy was razed to the ground by a fire at the end of the war. This fire was not reported in Homer's *The Iliad* – in fact, it was not even known about until 1871, when the German researcher **Heinrich Schlieman** excavated the ruins of the mythical walled city. Then, in the 1930s in the course of excavations led by the American archaeologist **Carl (William) Blegen** a further layer of the ruined city was discovered, and this layer (the seventh one from the surface) bore traces of burning – evidence that these hidden remains of the city of Troy were those of the time which Homer wrote about.

The siege of Troy

*As well as being the title of a poem by Homer, the word 'Odyssey' has become a word commonly used to mean a long journey or voyage, with many dangers and obstacles. The film director **Stanley Kubrick** used it in the title of his film fantasy **2001: A Space Odyssey** in 1968.*

> The poet who described a fantastic journey through hell and purgatory and on to Paradise

DANTE ALIGHIERI
(Florence 1265 – Ravenna 1321)

In the darkness, Dante could hardly make out the outline of the trees. He had got lost and now he could not go on. Quite still and full of fear he suddenly saw a light in the darkness, the first sign of dawn breaking. He began walking again. beginning the ascent up what seemed to be a hill. But, when he believed that he was safe at last, he found himself facing three wild animals, a lynx, a lion and a wolf, blocking his path. Then, in near despair, he heard voices – the first was the poet Virgil, and then his beloved Beatrice speaking to him from Paradise, both guiding him across to the afterlife, and so saving both his body and his soul.

It was the Easter weekend of 1300. Dante was 35 years old, when he began his imaginary **journey into the afterlife**. As Dante put it: 'In the middle of life, I came to a dark wood'. During this journey, he would be accompanied by the great Latin poet of ancient Roman times, Virgil – and the result would be *The Divine Comedy*, one of the most beautiful examples of world literature. Dante began writing it in about 1306, with the first part called *The Inferno*. He continued in 1308 with the writing of *Purgatory*, and the final draft of the third part, *Paradise*, was completed only a short time before his death in 1321.

Dante (a shortened form of the name Durante) Alighieri was born in Florence in 1265. His ancestors had been nobles in the city, trading as respected money-lenders. At the time of Dante's birth, his family were very poor. Despite this, Dante had lessons in language and grammar, before being taught by **Brunetto Latini**, a famous writer who taught languages and philosophy in Bologna, the university city where Dante stayed between 1286 and 1287. Some years before, in about 1283, he had begun to compose poems, under the influence of his friend Guido Cavalcanti. These gave birth to a complete, new poetical style which earned the name Dolce Stil Nuovo ('Sweet New Style'). Towards the end of the thirteenth century, Dante entered into the field of politics. This was the time of bitter conflicts between different

Dante meeting Father Ilarius

Dante on his death-bed

parties in Florence – the **Ghibellines**, who supported the Holy Roman Emperor and the **Guelfs**, who supported the Pope. In 1297, Dante wrote his first important work, *Arte dei Medici e degli Speziali*, and largely as a result of the fame he received, he was appointed to many important positions, such as City Magistrate. But by 1301, the situation in Florence had worsened and Dante, who was on the side of **Pope Boniface VIII**, had to flee from the Ghibellines, exiled from Florence by 1302. If he had dared return, he would have been burned at the stake. Instead, Dante had to move continuously from one city to another in northern Italy, seeking protection and support.

After being at Forlì, Arezzo, Lucca and Verona, he arrived at Ravenna, where he became ill (perhaps of malaria) and died in 1321.

Dante and Virgil in a painting by Flores

All the numbers of the Divine Comedy

For the Roman Catholic church of the Middle Ages, certain numbers had a particular significance. For example, **three** represented the Holy Trinity of God as the Father, the Son and the Holy Ghost, whilst **ten** was the symbol of perfection. That is why these two numbers recur in all the complex structure of Dante's *Comedy*, comprising three parts – the *Inferno*, *Purgatory* and *Paradise*, each part comprising 33 chapters. The final chapter comprises 99 verses (33 x 3), in a total of 100 chapters – that is, 10 multiplied by 10 – absolute perfection!

The love of a woman

In the poetry and in the *Prosimetro* (a book where pieces of prose and poetry are mixed together) of *La Vita Nuova* (The New Life) Dante expresses his love in meeting Beatrice, the noble Florentine lady, **Bice di Folco Portinari**. He had met her for the first time when she was nine years old, and in his writings, he gives her the image of a heavenly messenger, an angel – rather than his wife **Gemma Donati**, who bore him four children. In Dante's *Divine Comedy*, Beatrice also becomes a forerunner of theology, which is the study of God and religion. And so, the earthly love which Dante had for Beatrice became one which existed in Paradise.

Dante in the Afterlife, fresco by Domenico di Michelino

Miniature depicting Dante and Virgil in *The Inferno*

The creator of the 'mad' Don Quixote, wandering knight, Man of La Mancha

MIGUEL DE CERVANTES

(Alcalá de Henares 1547 – Madrid 1616)

In a corner of the prison cell, crouched on a filthy mattress, a man gave a burst of crazy laughter. Outside the heavy iron door, a guard told him to be quiet at once. Cervantes obeyed, but his eyes continued to gleam with excitement. For a time he had given up counting the slow passing of the hours, days and months. He was no longer conscious of the foul smell of the latrines, the scuttling of mice, the screaming of other prisoners and the solitude. Instead, he saw sunlit fields, smoky inns, sweet children and starry skies – because, as he awoke each day, this prisoner became Don Quixote, a fearless knight who crossed the warm countryside of Spain in his unending search for new adventure.

In 1602, Miguel de Cervantes was **imprisoned in Seville** accused of fraud. This was an experience which he overcame by creating the adventure stories which we can still enjoy today – tales of duels, battles, attacks by pirates and daring fights. With his rich imagination, Cervantes created **Don Quixote** as the main character in his most successful and famous book. Cervantes was able to tell the incredible story of this knight errant (wandering knight), because he himself had been a restless vagabond and was always an incurable dreamer.

Cervantes' own adventures began during the first years of his life, when, together with his family, he moved from Salamanca to Seville, and, later on, to Madrid. In 1568, when he had just begun to write, he journeyed to Rome, not on a sight-seeing trip, but to flee from punishment. Cervantes had wounded a man in a duel, and the penalty for this was a hand being chopped off and then the offender being sent into exile.

In Italy, Cervantes began his military career, taking part in 1571 in the **Battle of Lepanto** against the Turks. In 1575, during his return journey to Spain, he was captured by **pirates** and taken to

Algeria, where he remained in **slavery** for over five years. Returning to Spain, he had several more battles with the law and also had to face still more money problems. At his death, which happened one year after the publication of the second part of *Don Quixote* (1615), Cervantes left behind an incredible quantity of valuable works. As well as his most famous book, he had composed many plays – such as *Eight Comedies* and *Eight New Interludes* and short stories such as *Exemplary Tales*.

An epic battle

In 1571, Cervantes took part in what became regarded as one of the true crusades – the Battle of Lepanto (shown in painting, below). In contrast to the Holy Crusades of the Middle Ages, the reason for this battle was not to take control of the Holy Land but the Mediterranean Sea. Many European countries, their sea traffic threatened by the ships of the Ottoman (Turkish) Emperor Selim II, formed a 'Holy League' to confront the whole of the Turkish fleet. During the Battle of Lepanto, Cervantes, a soldier under the command of Diego de Urbino, was seriously injured in one hand.

The ideals of a knight

Don Quixote by Picasso

Perhaps the most famous pages of Don Quixote are those in which the brave knight goes into battle against the **windmills**. Deaf to the wise advice of his faithful squire Sancho Panza, the brave *hidalgo* (knight) spurs his horse, the unreliable and obstinate Ronsinate, towards those who, so Don Quixote believes, are giants with huge, spreading arms, blaming the whole situation on a spell by a wizard called Freston. The episode ends with Don Quixote crashing into the wooden sails of the windmills. This comic scene has led to the expression '**tilting at windmills**' which is used to describe the task of those who go into battle without first thinking about it. Don Quixote has become a champion of all the **idealists** who want to make the world a better place in which to live.

A LITTLE MORE INFORMATION ...

In his play **Vita ad Algeri**, *Cervantes describes the time he spent as a slave in Algeria. He identified with one of the leading characters in the play,* **Saavedra**, *to such an extent that, after the play had been performed, Cervantes added the name of the character to his own.*

Scene from *Don Quixote*

Knights of madness

It seems that, with great knights, there is often a 'touch' of madness. This is what happened, for example, to the knight Don Quixote at the start of the novel by Cervantes, and also to Orlando, the main character in *Orlando Furioso* ('Orlando Enraged') a poem by the Italian writer **Ludovico Ariosto**. Don Quixote and Orlando 'lost their minds' for different reasons. The **madness** of Don Quixote was more the eccentricity which came about through his desire to be a 'wandering knight'; whereas Orlando's madness was because he had lost the love of the beautiful Angelica. They also came to their senses in different ways. Don Quixote came down to earth after a duel, whilst Orlando was saved by his friend Astolpho who rose up to the Moon in the chariot of the prophet Elijah in order to reclaim Orlando's sanity.

The man who wrote plays and tragedies which revealed the human mind

WILLIAM SHAKESPEARE
(Stratford-on-Avon 1564 – 1616)

The door of the house slammed violently. Even as Shakespeare strode away, he could still hear the angry voice of his wife, the clamour of his baby daughter and the irritated crying of the twins. Gradually, his own anger cooled, giving way to a sense of desperation. 'Responsibilities, Will, nothing but responsibilities. That is your only prospect for the future,' he murmured to himself. He walked quickly towards the fields, thinking of the heroes of the past, of their courage and their determination. That made him feel sorry for himself, sad about his fears and his hesitation. The following day, the theatrical company would leave Stratford, taking with them his shattered dreams. Unless …

Soon after the birth of his twins, a son and a daughter, in 1585, William Shakespeare left his birth-place, Stratford-on-Avon for London. Whether this was in order to escape from a harsh punishment

The Globe Theatre, London

if he were found guilty of fraud – or, more probably, because he wanted to abandon a family life which was becoming too heavy to bear, we do not know. (At only twenty years old, he had to provide for a wife and three children). What is certain is that, by 1592, he had become firmly settled in the world of the London theatre, working as an **actor**. In the years which followed, Shakespeare set aside the acting profession, taking up a career as a **playwright**. Although he had attended Grammar School at Stratford, Shakespeare had not been educated to university level. Yet, within a short time he had read the chronicles of the historian **Raphael Holinshead**, whose work he later **dramatized**, and made many contacts among the artists with university backgrounds. All this enabled Shakespeare to bridge the cultural gap which separated him from established writers, such as **Christopher Marlowe**. In 1595, Shakespeare became a member of the famous **theatrical company of the Lord Chancellor**, which gave him the opportunity of becoming known at the royal court, becoming friends with noble and influential people. At this time, the number of people going to the theatre was increasing rapidly, and Shakespeare's name soon became widely known as the writer of fine plays. Before long, he was acclaimed as the greatest playwright who ever lived, an honour which remains to this day. With his fame came new-found riches, due largely to the profits which he made by becoming part owner of the **Globe Theatre**. This new and unexpected wealth enabled him to

The house where Shakespeare was born

obtain a coat of arms for his house as well as buying a new home, which he called *New Place* at Stratford. This house became the place where he liked to think, an oasis of peace where he could retreat from London and find inspiration for his writing. It was at *New Place* that, at the beginning of the seventeenth century, he wrote his most famous plays, such as *Hamlet, Othello* and *Macbeth*, and where, from 1611, he established his permanent home until his death on 23 April 1616.

From stage to screen

Scene from the film *Shakespeare in Love*

A Midsummer Night's Dream – Theatre production

In days gone by, the only way of seeing the works of Shakespeare was to go to a theatre. Now we can enjoy the plays of this great English writer, sitting comfortably in our own homes. This is all thanks to the cinema, television, and, of course, Shakespeare, the writer whose plays are based on themes which are still relevant today. One of the first to play a Shakespearean role on the 'big screen' was the British actor and director **Laurence Olivier**, followed by others such as **Orson Welles** and **Franco Zeffirelli**, all staying close to the dress and the settings of Shakespeare's time. In recent years, however, there have been new and more adventurous experiments in the cinema. Some directors have preferred to put Shakespeare's words into a modern-day setting – film-documentaries such as *Richard III, A Man and a King* by **Al Pacino**; musicals such as Cole Porter's *Kiss Me Kate* and *Pens of Lost Loves* directed by **Kenneth Branagh**, as well as montages of fantasy, such as a version of *Romeo and Juliet*, where the tender-hearted young Romeo becomes a misfit on *Verona beach*.

Writers and fighters

As well as plays with imaginary settings, many others were based on everyday situations which Shakespeare observed in every detail. These details prove to us that the world in which he lived and moved, and about which he wrote, was far from being a happy and peaceful place. In the sixteenth century (an era dominated by Queen Elizabeth I) England was a nation where secret plots within Royal palaces, assassinations and violence of every type were the order of the day. Therefore it is not surprising that even actors and writers were often involved in criminal episodes. This is what happened to two great interpreters of Elizabethan theatre – **Christopher Marlowe** and **Ben Jonson**, both restless men who lived their lives to the very limit of the law. Marlowe, who was engaged by the throne as a secret agent, was accused of having killed a man. But before he could be arrested, he was assassinated most mysteriously. Jonson managed to avoid a harsh punishment for murder only by fleeing the country.

The Foxes
by Ben Jonson

A scene from *Tamburlaine the Great* by Christopher Marlowe

Romeo and Juliet by Angelo Inganni

Juliet's balcony in Verona

Shakespeare and Italy

There have always been arguments among students of English literature as to whether Shakespeare ever travelled to **Italy**. By staying in some Italian cities, he might have got the idea for many of his works which are set there, and which are accurate both in description and their geographic location, as well as in the social life and politics of the time. The **Venice** of *Othello* and *The Merchant of Venice*; the **Verona** of *Romeo and Juliet* and *The Two Gentlemen of Verona*; **Messina**, for *Much Ado About Nothing* and **Padua**, for *The Taming of the Shrew* are some of the most famous examples. Although we lack any written evidence to confirm the presence of Shakespeare in Italy, it is highly probable that he underwent a journey to the warm Italian countryside for the benefit of his mental, rather than physical health – to put new life into his dreams and to open his eyes to books and manuscripts written by foreign authors.

Below left, Hamlet and Horatio at the graveyard

Above left, the character of Shylock in *The Merchant of Venice*

Left, Macbeth meets the three witches

Famous quotations

'Something is rotten in the state of Denmark' (**Hamlet**): at the beginning of the play, the young Prince Hamlet is aware that something horrible is about to happen, even though nothing yet shows this.

'To be or not to be: that is the question.' (**Hamlet**): this phrase opens the famous monologue in which Hamlet tries to decide if he should commit suicide. After having been almost convinced of this extreme gesture, he maintains that to die is a little like going to sleep … ('death, to sleep; to sleep, perchance to dream') decides not to kill himself, frightened of what he may find beyond death.

'Romeo! Romeo! Oh, wherefore art thou, Romeo?' (**Romeo and Juliet**): words spoken by Juliet at the beginning of the balcony scene. Having discovered that she is in love with a member of a rival family, she asks her loved one to answer to his name, because - 'A rose by any other name would smell as sweet'.

'I hold the world but as the world, Gratiano; a stage where every man must play a part. And mine a sad one.' (**Merchant of Venice**): the words with which Antonio grieves that each person has his or her own fate.

The jealousy of Othello

Othello and Desdemona

In his play *Zaira* (1773), the writer **Voltaire** re-tells the drama of *Othello*, the Shakespearean tragedy on the theme of jealousy, where the Moor of Venice (Othello) is in love with the beautiful Desdemona and is persuaded by the evil Iago to believe that his young wife has been unfaithful to him with Cassio. In a letter written in 1823, the Italian writer **Alessandro Manzoni** underlined the superiority of the Shakespearean text to that of Voltaire. Manzoni criticized Voltaire, saying that he had made the beginnings of jealousy in the main character too direct. In *Othello*, this part of the drama sprang from rumour and Othello's belief in the false evidence provided by Iago (an innocent handkerchief); whereas in *Zaira*, the main character's suspicion of unfaithfulness by his wife was borne out by the existence of a letter.

The death of Ophelia

Ophelia, the young sweetheart of Hamlet in Shakespeare's play, died by drowning herself in a river. Her tragic end has been the source of inspiration for many artists, especially in the nineteenth century.

Left, *Ophelia* by Millais
Below, *The Death Of Ophelia* by Delacroix
Right, *Ophelia* by Waterhouse

Love in verse

Love, the emotion which is woven into the plots of all Shakespeare's plays, is also at the centre of his poems: **154 sonnets** refer to the relationship between a **fair youth** and a **dark lady**, a cruel and mysterious woman.

The writer who was torn between the structure of the ancient classics and the originality and realism of the 'Age of Enlightenment'

JOHANN WOLFGANG GOETHE

(Frankfurt 1749 – Weimar 1832)

The sound of hooves on the cobbles and the screech of wheels echoed along the street of the sleeping city. Almost everything was in darkness, the way barely lit by faint moonbeams. Inside the carriage, Goethe looked for the last time on the outline of the houses of Weimar. His mind went back to the time when, ten years before, he had arrived with such enthusiasm for the German city. He hated going away like this from the court of Duke Karl August and his beloved Charlotte, but he knew that the time had come for him to undertake his long-awaited journey to Italy, to see for himself the greatness of the classical ancient arts.

In 1786, at the time of leaving Weimar, Johann Wolfgang Goethe was the famous author of the book *The Sorrows of the Young Werther*. Over ten years earlier, in 1775, he had been appointed by Duke Karl August to enrich the cultural life of his court. After a long **journey through Italy** which lasted two years (1786 – 1788), he returned a more mature artist, a person who seemed to have little in common with those he had left behind in Weimar. Fascinated by the beauty and grace of the Greek-Roman art which he had seen during his travels, Goethe tried, together with his friend, the writer **Friedrich Schiller** to recapture the classic art of ancient times. But although he became well-known as a promoter of classic art, at heart Goethe still remained a more imaginative writer, not so far removed from the shy little boy that he had once been, enchanted by the puppet theatre and who, as a university student, preferred the literature of **Shakespeare** to the boring lessons of law. In his most successful work of later years, *Faust*, (a play which he finished only one year before his death) and

Goethe in the Roman Countryside, painted by Tischbein

Goethe in Rome, painted by Hackert

Wilhelm Meister (a book which remained for decades on his writing desk) he clearly gives us clues about the original, imaginative side of his nature which his taste for classical art never quite overcame. In his old age, Goethe became a source of reference for the new generation of writers, both German and other nationalities. His house at **Weimar** was transformed into a 'postal exchange' of correspondence and messages from every part of Europe and Goethe received many visitors, both from Germany and other countries. The work of Goethe influenced a large part of European literature which was written during the years which followed.

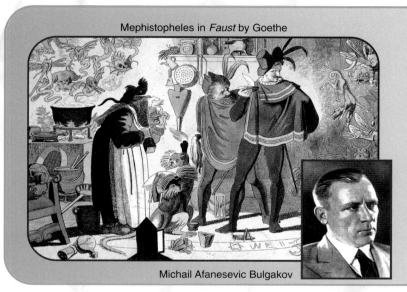
Mephistopheles in *Faust* by Goethe

Michail Afanesevic Bulgakov

The girl and the devil

The plot of *Faust*, the monumental play by Goethe, revolved around **Margherita**, the woman loved with overwhelming passion by the main character, Doctor Faust. In the twentieth century, the writer **Michail Afanasevic Bulgakov** made Margherita one of the main characters in his work *I Master I Margarita* (The Master and Margarita) a novel set in a Russia which was dominated by suspicion within all parts of society. But Michail Bulgakov's Margarita has more independence than the Margherita in Faust. When the 'Master' is sent to the psychiatric ward for trying to portray the story of Jesus, it is Margarita who, by the end of the book, has secured his freedom.

Scientific Interests

As well as poetry, plays and books, Goethe was also a respected writer on scientific subjects, particularly botany and biology. He also showed that he had considerable gifts as a researcher when, in 1784, he identified a **bone of a human skeleton**. This was the intermaxillare, which, as we now know, is the bone between the upper and lower jaw. Although Goethe was not the first to identify this bone, he did not know this, and so arrived at

his conclusion quite independently of the findings by any other researcher. His achievement made him much admired in scientific circles, and his efforts were even recognized by the renowned naturalist from Britain, **Charles Darwin**.

The craze for 'sorrows'

The publication in 1774 of *Young Werther's Sorrows*, Goethe's first novel, created a sensation in the society of the time. The tragic story of the main character who **committed suicide for love**, inflamed the hearts and minds of readers throughout Europe. Many young men began to copy the features of the main character – the way he dressed, his search for solitude, even his self-destruction – and this became such a problem that some city councillors banned circulation of the book. Nevertheless, its success was enormous, and soon after it was published, *Young Werther's Sorrows* became a model for many foreign authors. The events described by Werther were re-told, for example, by the Italian writer **Ugo Foscolo** in *The Last Letters of Jacopo Ortis* (1802).

Libretto of the opera *Werther*

Goethe in his studio

> *The novelist who could create the most dramatic characters and atmospheres*

FËODOR MIKHAILOVICH DOSTOYEVSKI

(Moscow 1821 – Petersburg 1881)

The ice penetrated like a sharp blade between the boards of the hut. The dismal howl of the wind combined with the rhythmic snoring of the sleeping group. But sleep would not come to the young man. Instead, his anxious mind seemed to be wandering in the darkness, caught up in the feeling of some terrible foreboding. Another crisis was coming, he was sure of it. Perhaps it would not happen during the night, probably not even the next day, but the feeling which had gripped him for several days was a clear sign that it was all happening again. As he slowly sank into a state of sleep, he seemed to feel hands which grasped at his clothes, snatches of conversation, gunshot and mad laughter whirling around in his head. He wanted to scream, but fear trapped his voice in his throat. Then there came a cry – and he found himself standing beside his bed.

In 1849, Fëodor Michailovich Dostoyevski was arrested on a charge of political treason and of having been a member of a party which was plotting a revolution. For this, he was **condemned to death**. Although the sentence was immediately commuted to eight years' imprisonment (later, four years' hard labour), he learned of this only after he had been taken to the place of execution and stood in front of the firing squad, believing that he was going to be killed. This dramatic event left its terrible mark on his life and his art.

Soon afterwards, Dostoyevski was beginning to discover the horrors of Siberia. In the **detention camp of Omsk** where he was interned in 1850, he had to face many hardships and much suffering. His desperate situation was made even worse by the debilitating disability of **epilepsy**, which would affect both his body and his mind for the rest of his life. Dostoyevski first met with tragedy in 1839. While he was at the Academy of Military Engineering at St. Petersburg, he was informed that his father had died (some say assassinated by his servants). Dostoyevski had both hated and feared his father, who was a good parent but a very stern-minded, harsh man. But, although Dostoyevski had never been close to his father, he felt so guilty about his death that he felt that he wanted to die, blaming

Dostoyevski's home

Sonya in *Crime and Punishment*

himself for what had happened.

These confused feelings which Dostoyevski felt for his father are also present in one of his masterpieces, *The Brothers Karamazov*, a story which centres around the murder of a father. In 1864 another death, this time, his brother, Mikhail, made him sink again into **despair**. Dostoyevski also had to face the failure of a journal founded by the two brothers, *The Epoch*, which collapsed due to Mikhail's death, more money worries adding to a financial situation which was already serious. But gradually, Dostoyevski began to recover, writing works which were highly critical of the regime of the Russian Tsar. For many years, in order to succeed in the publication of his works, Dostoyevski was forced to **flee to foreign parts** to avoid being arrested, not only due to the enemies he made in the court of the Tsar, but also because of the numerous debts he incurred. Only towards the end of his life did he succeed in earning a bare minimum to live in peace. In addition, he was able to leave the money worries and the everyday agonies and anxieties which had always persecuted him to his faithful and devoted wife Anna. However, all the devastating events and tragedies he had encountered continued to give him plenty of inspiration for his writing, and the themes of approaching death and cruel punishment are portrayed in many of his most successful books, such as *The Demons, Crime and Punishment, The Idiot* and *The Brothers Karamazov*.

An Expanse of Misery

For four long years, Dostoyevski, condemned to hard labour for having sympathies with 'rebel' political parties, had to suffer the harsh life of the **Siberian detention camps**. In the city of Omsk, where he arrived at the beginning of 1850, he discovered a harsh world of cold and hunger, populated by desperate, embittered people. The terrible life he had experienced and seen in Siberia became the central theme of his book entitled *Memories of a House of the Dead* (1861 – 1862). Even almost a century after the time of Dostoyevski, the lives of the prisoners in Siberian labour camps had not changed very much. The government of the Tsar had been overthrown in the Revolution of 1917 by the Bolsheviks – and although they opposed the whole Tsarist regime, prisoners continued to be deported to Siberia for many, many years. One of these prisoners, the writer **Aleksandr Solzhenitsyn**, denounced the cruelty which was still being perpetuated in his book *Archipelago Gulag* (1974).

Forced labour
in Siberia

The novelist who described the world of the 'miserable ones' – the thieves, the gypsies, the cripples …

VICTOR HUGO

(Besançon 1802 – Paris 1885)

The empty theatre had an air of expectancy. The last candle was about to be lit, whilst the valets in their livery stood in the corridors, ready to admit the public. A few moments more, and then the silence would be swamped by the chatter of women and the pompous conversation of noble gentlemen. But, at this moment the entire theatre belonged only to him, the playwright, who stood alone on the stage. Within a few hours, his fate would be sealed. Applause would mean glory. Cat-calls, whistles, or – worse – indifference, and it would be the end of his literary career.

From the first performance on 25 February 1830, the play *Hernani* by Victor Hugo was a great hit with the theatre-going public. The author, for whom this work was to launch a **challenge to the classical theatre of the Comédie Française**, was shortly to become a leading light of the French romantic movement: and so, the words came true which he had said when he was only fourteen years old, 'I want to be Chateaubriand or nothing', which was the equivalent of saying 'I want to be the number one'. The desire for artistic achievement developed in Hugo while he was still young. When his work earned him his **first literary acknowledgements**, this was enough for his father, one of Napoleon Bonaparte's Generals, to admit that the young Victor was better suited to becoming a good writer than a good soldier.

In 1830, the year in which Hugo reached new literary heights with *Hernani*, he also began his book *Notre Dame de Paris*, his first romantic novel. After writing poetry and then plays, he started on story-telling, a field of literature in which he reached worldwide fame with *Les Miserables* (1862). As well as his commitment to the arts, Hugo also took an active part in the political life of France. It was because of this, that in 1851 he was forced into exile, where he remained for almost twenty years until 1870. On his death in 1885, the greatness of his literary works earned him the honour of being taken in triumph to the **Pantheon** in Paris, where the most noble and the most famous French citizens are entombed.

Esmeralda and Quasimodo in *Notre Dame de Paris*

Hugo and the modern theatre

In the preface of his verse drama *Cromwell* in 1827, Hugo adopted the style of the imaginative romantic writers, turning against two of the three **'golden rules' of classical theatre** – keeping to the same time and the same place throughout the play. In the Greek tragedies, writers were allowed just one set, and the action portrayed in the play took place within just one day in the lives of the characters. According to Hugo, these limitations made the play seem unrealistic. Was it, in fact, possible that a man madly in love with a woman could come to his own murder all within the space of a few hours? And how could it happen that all the individuals present in one place – for example, a castle – could always meet in the same room? Hugo's view was that the playwright had to feel free to use times and places which are relevant to the background and development of the actual play.

Poster for *Hernani*, a play by Victor Hugo

Political battles

Hugo did not just write about the sad plight of the 'miserable ones' in his books and plays, he also committed himself firmly to their cause in real life, hoping that the dismal existence of the many unfortunate French citizens who struggled to exist on the edges of society could be made better. His progressive political ideas (abolition of the death penalty, freedom of speech, extension of civil rights, etc.) brought him into conflict with the government established by **Napoleon III**, who, elected President of the Republic of France in 1848, had established himself as Emperor. In 1851, Hugo was forced to flee the country, beginning a long exile which would end only with the death in 1870 of Napoleon's successor. During this time, Hugo continued his political battle, including making jokes of the new emperor in his book *Napoleon the Little One* (1852).

Illustration for *Les Miserables*

A fierce critic

Between 1935 and 1936, **Eugène Ionesco** (1912 – 1994), one of the leading interpreters of the so-called 'Theatre of the Absurd', wrote *The Grotesque Life and Tragedy of Victor Hugo*, a comedy-style biography of the French writer. At the time, Ionesco was a young writer driven more by the desire to make an impressive debut and to rise to the top in one fell swoop by breaking away from the ties of the past, than from a genuine wish to write a biography of the artistic and political life of Victor Hugo. Later, Ionesco maintained that his 'sacrilegious' gesture was directed against the 'myth' of Hugo and had not been meant to diminish the value of his works.

Photograph of the *Calva Singers* by Ionesco

CARTOON CHARACTERS

*The incredible lives of the gypsy girl Esmerelda, the hunch-backed bell-ringer Quasimodo, the cruel bishop Frollo and the brave captain Phoebus, as told in the book 'Notre Dame de Paris' by Victor Hugo, inspired an animated film made by **Walt Disney** entitled 'The Hunchback of Notre Dame' (1996). The difference was that the tragic deaths of the characters were changed into a more romantic theme, where 'they all lived happy ever after'.*

Statue from Notre Dame cathedral

A LIFE CUT SHORT

The writer who investigated the most hidden zones of the human mind

EDGAR ALLAN POE
(Boston 1809 – Baltimore 1849)

Edgar Allen Poe was a genius, whose rich imagination created a **world of horror**. He died over a century before the success of books written by authors such as Stephen King, which create the tense atmosphere and dramatic happenings that were so common in Poe's works. Tragedy dogged

The Pit and the Pendulum

the life of Edgar Allen Poe. He lost many of the people he loved – including his mother, who died when he was very young, both his adoptive parents and his adored wife. Throughout his existence, he was always being confronted with the peril of madness. Born in Boston in 1809 to theatrical parents who travelled around, he died in 1849, desperate and alone, in a Baltimore hospital, where he had been taken in a state of **physical breakdown and mental delirium**. Within

these forty years, he led a sad, despairing life, made worse by taking an excess of alcohol and drugs (opium), the effects of which he wrote about in stories and poems, depicting in agonizing realism the desperation of the human mind confronted by fear and death. One example of this is in the story *The Tell Tale Heart*, when the main character, who is responsible for a terrible murder, says: I have listened many times to the perils of going to Hell. But, why *will* you say that *I* am mad?

Animals of the Night

Its black plumage and an ugly croak has made the raven a **symbol of death**. This parallel was used by Edgar Allan Poe when he titled his most famous poem *The Raven*. In this poem, the raven is a messenger from Hell, and it appears as if suddenly emerging from the darkness, in a stanza of the poem in which the words 'never more' are repeated over and over again, and in which the main character is trying to bring his beloved Lenore back to life. Ideas inspired by the lyrics of Poe were made into a film in 1994 *The Raven* – a black comedy where the main character, the dead Erik Draven returns to the world of the living to revenge himself for his own death and that of his sweetheart.

Illustration from The Raven

STRANGE FACT
The actor playing the part of 'The Raven', Brandon Lee (son of the famous martial arts expert Bruce Lee), died on the set during the filming of a shoot-out, killed by a bullet from a pistol, which was believed to have been safe to fire. The person responsible for this incident (perhaps murder) has never been named.

MUSICIANS
and
COMPOSERS

> *The most famous of all in a family of fine musicians*

JOHANN SEBASTIAN BACH

(Eisenach 1685 – Leipzig 1750)

His fingers hovered over the keys. In his mind, Bach went through the work he was about to play. He felt nervous at the prospect of playing for such a great king, more nervous than he had felt for years. Behind him, the people at court chatted as they waited. At last the entrance of the king was announced and silence fell as everyone rose to their feet and bowed. Taking his seat, Frederick II signalled with his hand that the lords and ladies were now permitted to sit. Then he asked Bach to begin the recital. And, as his hands began running over the keys, Bach's nervousness vanished. Instead, there was only the most beautiful music.

In 1747, Johann Sebastian Bach was cantor (director of music) of the Church of Saint Thomas in Leipzig. This was the year when Bach decided to visit his son Emanuel at Potsdam, in eastern Germany. Potsdam was then the royal residence of the King of Prussia (now part of Germany), **Frederick II 'The Great'**, who, as well as being a powerful sovereign and a military expert, was also a fine musician. He invited Bach to play for him, to create melodies on a musical theme suggested by His Majesty and which Bach later wrote down in a composition called *The Musical Offering*.

When he visited Potsdam, Bach was approaching the last years of his life. He was glad to see that his son was well settled in the Prussian court as an accomplished player of the clavichord. Now, he knew, the musical tradition of the family was certain to continue.

Johann Sebastian had been born in 1685, the son of Johann Ambrosius Bach, who, like most of his **ancestors** was an outstanding musician. At the early death of his father, the young Bach was looked after by his elder brother Johann Christoph. His brother had been a pupil of the famous composer **Johann Pachelbel**, and he passed on all he had learned to Johann Sebastian. In 1700, Bach became a **chorister** at

Above left, a recital by Bach; left, Bach playing for Frederick II

the Church of Saint Michael at Lüneburg, and continued his studies as a musician. Three years later, at only eighteen years old, he was appointed organist at Arnstadt, an important position. He was soon recognized as being such an outstanding musician that he was often chosen to play for members of royal families and other famous and important people. Bach moved from place to place many times during his life. He accepted each new appointment with the aim of improving his social position as well as extending his knowledge of music, although he was often involved in arguments and disputes with those he worked for. After having lived at Mülhausen, Weimar and Köthen, in 1723, Bach settled in **Leipzig**, where he died in 1750.

A family of musicians

According to Bach in his writing *The Origins of the Bach Family*, the generations of outstanding musicians began with an Hungarian called Veit, who fled his native land for religious reasons and settled in Wechmar, Germany. Although he became a **miller**, Veit also had a taste for good music and was an excellent player of the lyre. He and his brothers had an excellent **musical ear** – Hans Veit, a bricklayer by trade, was also a fine stage jester, whilst Caspar was a gifted trombone player. This talent for music was passed from generation to generation until Johann Sebastian Bach (who inherited it from his father Johann Ambrosius, organist at Eisenach) passed it on to his many sons, in particular to Wilhelm Friedemann, Carl Philipp Emanuel and Johann Christian.

Bach with some of his sons

Bach in prison

In the winter of 1717, Bach spent almost one month (from 6 November to 2 December) in Weimar prison. The trouble began when the Director of Music at Weimar died. Bach expected to succeed him, and when the Duke of Weimar did not appoint him, Bach resigned his post as organist and accepted the post as Director of Music to **Prince Leopold of Köthen**. The Duke refused Bach's resignation, insisting instead that there should be a competition between Bach and a famous French organist **Louis Marchand**. When Marchand did not appear, Bach again asked permission to leave Weimar. But the Duke was remembering a previous occasion in 1707 when Bach had wanted to leave Arnstadt and had succeeded. The Duke of Weimar was determined

that this valuable musician should not leave the employment of his family a second time – hence the imprisonment at Weimar. This was not the first time (nor would it be the last) that the composer would come into conflict with his employers. But at Weimar, he showed more than on any other occasion, the full strength of his determination and his pride and in the end he succeeded in leaving the employ of the Duke.

Organ recital

Determined, up to his death

By 1749, Bach's health was so poor that many thought he would die. He had almost **lost his sight**, and as he spent most of his time in his own home, some people came to the conclusion that he had suffered a heart attack. The Council at Leipzig therefore decided it was time to begin searching for a composer to succeed him. After a performance on 8 June, they chose the university organist, Johann Gottlieb Görner. When Bach heard of this appointment, he flew into such a rage that his would-be successor left the city.

The city of Leipzig

The genius of a composer and musician whose work and life scandalized society

WOLFGANG AMADEUS MOZART

(Salzburg 1756 – Vienna 1791)

A few drops of holy water sprinkled on the coffin and a short prayer was all that commemorated the last journey of the composer. Nobody sang, no sound broke the silence. It was almost as if the whole world was stunned. No music, it seemed, was worthy of the dead master. At the end of the funeral, the few friends who had gathered around the coffin moved sadly away, leaving the hearse to begin moving towards the graveyard. There, the body was thrown into a pit where others had already been placed. From that moment, nobody could ever weep over the mortal remains of Mozart. But the greatest of all composers would live forever, through the notes of his wonderful music.

The funeral of Wolfgang Amadeus Mozart took place on 6 December 1791. It was not a great occasion, but a lonely burial in a common grave. Mozart, the musician and composer, had been acclaimed as a **child prodigy**, and yet he had died, his passing almost unnoticed, at only thirty five years old, his life ending in poverty and illness.
Mozart was born in 1756. His father was Leopold Mozart, Director of Music at Salzburg and Wolfgang learned to play the clavichord when he was only three years old. Accompanied by his father and his sister Maria Anna, who was also musical, in 1760 he played in the presence of **Queen Maria Theresa of Austria**. This performance was the first of a long series of recitals by the young Mozart in many European cities – first, in Germany, followed by Paris, London and Italian cities. But once he reached adult age, praise and acknowledgement was soon replaced by **jealous**

critics and only mild enthusiasm by the public. Often involved in disputes with his clients (his arguments with the Archbishop of Salzburg Cathedral are famous), he was soon reduced to living in hardship, squandering what money he earned on parties and entertainment in a style far above his means. He moved to Vienna in 1781, and here, as his life moved slowly towards its end, he composed music in a frenzy of creative activity. Among the works written at this time are some of his finest operas, such as *The Marriage of Figaro*, *Don Giovanni* and *The Magic Flute*, as well as his famous *Requiem*.

View of Salzburg

Mozart's 'Swan-Song'

It is said that the swan sings only once, just before it dies. When Mozart died, he had written the music for a **Funeral Mass**. This work remained unfinished, until it was completed by the composer Franz Xavier Süssmayr. This composition, the *Requiem* is surrounded in a cloud of mystery. Mozart himself added to this, maintaining – perhaps in the throes of sickness – that a mysterious person, maybe an angel or maybe a messenger from the Devil, had commissioned the work. Some people have suggested that Mozart sensed he was about to die, and so wanted to leave his own **swan song**, music written to accompany his own burial.

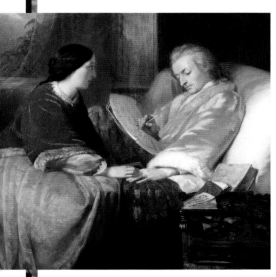
Mozart composing the *Requiem*

Mozart spoke Italian

The meeting between Mozart and **Lorenzo Da Ponte** (the 'pen name' of the Italian writer Emanuel Congegliano) happened in about 1785. From this meeting there blossomed an artistic partnership which resulted in Da Ponte writing the wonderful lyrics for three of Mozart's operas – *The Marriage of Figaro* (1786), *Don Giovanni* (1787) and *Così Fan Tutte* ('Everybody does it') (1790). The Italian librettist held the position of 'official poet' to the Emperor Joseph II at Vienna and he had also worked with other famous composers such as **Salieri** and **Martin y Solar**. But in Mozart, Da Ponte found a 'soul mate', someone with the same tastes in culture, nature and lifestyle. So, it is surprising that in his memoirs published in 1832 at the end of a long and colourful existence, he made only a brief mention of his dead composer friend.

The writer Lorenzo Da Ponte

The rage of Salieri

In *Amadeus*, the film made in 1984 by the director Milos Forman, the story is told of the meeting between Mozart and the mean-minded jealousy of his enemy, a lesser composer who would never reach the heights of the young genius. In the film, the story is told by a defeated **Antonio Salieri**, who has already confessed to a priest the immense hatred he feels in the presence of the God-given talent of Mozart. The film records little more than a rumour which had begun to spread during the eighteenth century. According to this rumour, Salieri was so jealous of Mozart and his incredible abilities, that he might have been guilty of his murder. This story flourished because of all the suspicion and rivalry which there was between the musicians and the composers at the Viennese court at the time. In his letters, Mozart writes with affection for Salieri, and there is no evidence that Salieri was at all cruel to him.

Scene from the film *Amadeus*

A sweet reminder of Mozart

In Austrian pastry shops, especially in Salzburg, Mozart's birth-place, among delicious sweets, such as the famous Sacher cakes, it is always possible to see piles of boxes of every shape and size, all with a picture of Mozart. These contain chocolate sweets dedicated to Mozart, the so-called **Mozart Balls**, made of the finest chocolate with a centre of green pistachio.

The composer who, when profoundly deaf, composed the famous Ode to Joy

LUDWIG VAN BEETHOVEN
(Bonn 1770 – Vienna 1827)

A faint whistle, like that of a distant train, persisted in his left ear. In the right ear, there was nothing at all. But although the pianist could not hear what he was playing, he carried on, running his hands over the keys, following the score. He was determined not to be beaten by his deafness, because without his music there would be no life left in him – and the God to whom he had prayed had now seen fit to take away the sense which was most precious of all, the sense of hearing. As his fingers pounded the keys, he could hear the notes in his mind, part of an unending melody. Although he was deaf, Beethoven's spirits were lifted up again by the music.

In 1798, Ludwig van Beethoven noticed the first symptoms of what would later be diagnosed as a **degenerative** (progressive) **loss of hearing**. He was only twenty eight years old and he would follow a long and sad path before he became completely deaf. But this disability did not prevent Beethoven from becoming a great musician, and – even more surprisingly – a prolific and gifted composer. In fact, he composed his most famous **symphonies** in his world of almost total silence. That he could do this was due not only to the genius of his musical talent, but also his thorough knowledge of music which he had developed during his youth.

The musical education of Beethoven, apart from his first apprenticeship at Bonn, his birth-place, took place in Vienna, the important centre of European music, where he moved in 1792. Although he could not benefit from the teaching of **Mozart**, whom he met only briefly in 1787,

Beethoven came under the wise guidance of **Joseph Haydn**, an equally famous composer. In 1795, it was Haydn who obtained for Beethoven his first official appointment – a series of dates to play at some masked balls. From that moment, thanks to the support of famous people and useful contacts with some publishing houses, he was able to dedicate his life completely to music – a decision which also landed him with long-standing money problems.

Beethoven's funeral

However, in his later years, his poverty was not in terms of money, but loneliness, lessened slightly by the presence in his house of his nephew Karl. The deafness, which had not prevented his music flourishing, had made him a timid and withdrawn man.

In praise of faithfulness

Leonora, a character in *Fidelio*

Beethoven composed only one opera – *Fidelio*. The libretto (book of the opera) was freely adapted from the play by the French writer **Jean-Nicolas Bouilly**. The opera tells the story of the dramatic life of Leonora, who has to wear men's clothes so that she can enter the prison at Seville and free her husband who has been unjustly imprisoned. After an unsuccessful start, the opera was greatly revised by Beethoven, and found favour with the public at its third production in 1814.

In passing ...

In Vienna, the lives of **Mozart**, the genius composer at the end of his life, troubled and suffering, and Beethoven, the rising star in the world of music, came briefly together. The two composers were so different, both in character and temperament, and so there was no possibility of an instant attraction – also, Beethoven had to leave Vienna in 1787 after a stay of only a few months. However, Mozart was able to be present at some of Beethoven's performances and recognized his talent, predicting that one day Beethoven would 'be spoken of, all over the world'.

Mozart and Beethoven

Beethoven Frieze by Klimt

Ode to Joy

Of all the symphonies composed by Beethoven, the ninth (and last) is one of the most famous and the one which received the most praise. Beethoven dedicated this symphony to the Prussian King **Frederick Wilhelm III**, for which he was rewarded by a precious ring as a gift from the sovereign. What is most surprising is that this symphony was written when the composer was almost completely deaf. Despite the misery which the loss of hearing caused him, Beethoven somehow found the inner strength to write the music, and in particular his 'Ode to Joy', with words written by the poet **Friedrich Schiller**. A visual version of this was created in 1902 by the artist **Gustav Klimt** in his *Beethoven Frieze*, a huge mural divided into three parts, the last of which portrays the same theme of Joy – the sparkling heavens (on the shoulders of the angels to the left) and the heavenly kiss (on the right).

The composer who greatly increased the number of works for performance by the pianist

FRÉDÉRIC CHOPIN
(Zelazowa Wola, Warsaw 1810 – Paris 1849)

The fronds of the palm trees were already wet with dew. Beyond, the pale rays of the moon were reflected on the surface of the sea. Out in the sparkling night air, Chopin was lost in his memories, following the sad chain of his thoughts. Darkness almost hid the house behind him, where everyone else slept peacefully. For him, trying to concentrate on a melody which would not come, the night was a time of agony and of waiting. Alone and in the darkness, a tune began to form in his mind, one note following another. The sounds of the night crept into his soul, replacing disillusions with dreams and bitterness with hope.

The night was the time in which the sensitive and dreamlike soul of Frédéric Chopin was most soothed. In his *Nocturnes* he recreates the magical atmosphere which lightens the hours dominated by silence and darkness, and when the world, apparently asleep, awakes to visions of dreams and fantasy. In these works, full of tenderness and melancholy, there emerges the essence of this composer – his sadness at being so distant from his beloved Poland and his family, and his love for a life in which the threatening **menace of illness** would no longer be present. Chopin was born in 1810 in the tiny village of Zelazowa Wola in Poland. Until 1830, he lived in Warsaw, and it was here that he had decided as a boy that he would be a professional musician. By 1830, Chopin had made his way to Paris, which he later chose as his adoptive home, taking with him the traditional melodies of Poland.

Excluding only his journey to **Majorca** which he made with the French author **George Sand** (the pen name of a lady, Aurore

Suite de Valses sur les Motifs de F. CHOPIN Par PIERRE MULLER

Poster advertising a suite of waltzes by Chopin

Dudevant) in 1838, a short time in England in 1848 and a summer holiday in the little city of Nohant, the composer lived in Paris for the rest of his short life. Here he found the surroundings ideal for his music and his art, as well as making close friends and famous acquaintances, all of whom influenced his development both as a pianist and as a composer. Some of these, such as the artist **Eugène Delacroix**, were with him at his death, which happened in the early hours of 17 October 1849.

The composer in love

George Sand

Chopin and **George Sand**: the delicate pianist, engrossed in his music, and the extraordinary author, eccentric and passionate. Theirs was a long love affair (ten years) and very intense. For the love of Aurore Dudevant, the real name of this popular writer, Chopin had to battle against prejudice and against himself, his natural shyness and his values. George did not seem to be the woman for him. She was divorced, with a liking for wearing men's clothes, a cigar smoker and completely unconcerned about causing scandal. Yet Chopin loved her wholeheartedly, ready to risk everything, his career and the respect of his own family to be near her.

Listening to Chopin

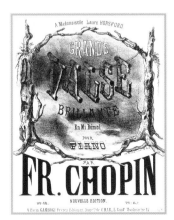
Cover of a piece of music by Chopin

Most of Chopin's compositions were written for the piano. Not counting the few works for orchestra and chamber music for small groups of players, his production was entirely dedicated to this instrument which, to quote the words of the famous pianist **Robert Alexander Schumann** could make sounds 'in a unique way'. As a composer, Chopin is best known for his **mazurkas** and **polkas**, traditional music from the country of his birth, Poland, and for his **nocturnes**, twenty one of these works dedicated to the night. In his repertoire there are also numerous waltzes, studies, ballads and sonatas.

The last goodbye

Chopin, who had never enjoyed good health, died at only thirty nine years old in October 1849. For many years, the cause of his death was believed to be consumption (tuberculosis), the disease of the lungs from which his younger sister Emilia also died; but some historians have suggested that he might have died as the result of an acute attack of asthma, brought on by an allergy. Whatever the cause, it is surprising that Chopin died in poverty. Although he was invited to give recitals and lessons in the homes of rich and important people and his music was an enormous success, Chopin, like Mozart, ended his life in the most extreme poverty. But unlike Mozart, Chopin had a dignified burial, preceded by a requiem mass where Mozart's *Requiem* was played.

The last moments in the life of Chopin

SAD MEMORIES

After the death of Chopin, his house was searched from top to bottom for unfinished compositions and incomplete works. Among the many sheets of music, a package tied with red ribbon was also found. This contained letters sent to the composer by Maria Wodzinski, the girl who was to have become his wife. Written on the package were the words **'moja bieda'** *('my disaster'), which reflects the deep sadness which Chopin felt after their engagement was broken off.*

The composer of operas who set to music some of the greatest masterpieces in literature

GUISEPPE VERDI
(Roncole di Busseto, Parma 1813 – Milan 1901)

Only a few moments remained before curtain-up. The musicians did their last-minute tuning-up. The high notes of the flute sounded together with the deep tone of the cornet, as the audience continued to come into the theatre. Verdi peeped out from the wings, his anxiety increasing as he watched people taking their places, on the terraces and up in the gallery. From those men and women who now chattered so casually, there would soon be triumph and glory or complete disinterest. 'Maestro! Time to go!' The whisper behind him reminded Verdi that the opera was about to start. The composer nodded and prepared himself for the beginning of the first act.

9 March 1842 saw the first performance of the dramatic opera by Giuseppe Verdi, *Nabucco* at the Scala, Milan. The composer, weakened by the death of his wife and two children, as well as the failure of a comic opera *One Day of the Kingdom*, was there with mixed feelings of anxiety and hope. As it happened, *Nabucco* was an incredible success. And so the composer, born less than thirty years before at Roncole di Busseto, a tiny village in the province of **Parma** made his triumphant entrance on the scene of Italian opera. He had spent many difficult years learning his art, during which time his parents had always been short of money to support him. But within a short time after the first night of *Nabucco*, Verdi had become a famous opera composer, applauded all over Italy as well as outside the country. Verdi was so enthusiastic about the dramatic content of his works that he often busied himself not only with the music, but also the libretto (words), sometimes interfering with the work of the writers and the set designers. Preparations for his spectacular opera *Aida*, in particular, took a long time. Verdi had been appointed to write *Aida* to celebrate the opening of the Suez Canal in 1870. The opera was set in **Cairo**, Egypt, and it opened in 1871.

In the latter years of his life, Verdi went to Sant' Agata (near to Busseto) more than anywhere else. Here he had bought a farm, where he would take a rest from the business of **Italian politics**, having been elected Senator in 1874. Before his death in 1901, he decreed that a part of his wealth was to be used to build a house of rest for musicians in Milan, the town where he was buried.

Above left, Verdi takes his oath at Parliament; right, the composer in the garden of his villa.

From book to the theatre

The success of some operas composed by Verdi, as well as the dramatic power of the music, was partly due to his choice of subject, which he often created around the theme of a famous romance or theatrical play. For example – **I Masnadieri** ('The Robbers') in 1847, based on the tragedy by Friedrich Schiller; **Rigoletto** in 1851, an adaptation of a theatrical piece by Victor Hugo *Le Roi s'amuse* (the king amuses himself); **La Traviata** in 1853, inspired by a book written by the French author **Alexander Dumas** *La Signora delle camelie* ('The Lady of the Camellias'); **Falstaff** in 1893, taking parts from Shakespeare's *Henry IV* and *The Merry Wives of Windsor*; **Hernani** (1844) based on the drama by **Victor Hugo**; *Luisa Miller* (1849) based on the tragedy by **Friedrich Schiller** '*Kabale und Liebe*' ('Kabale and Love'); *Macbeth* and *Othello* by **William Shakespeare** … the list goes on.

A curse – and what happened after

From childhood, Verdi demonstrated that he had a proud and fiery nature. He liked to remember an episode which happened when he was about six years old. One day, whilst helping the priest during a religious ceremony, Verdi forgot to hand him the flasks with the holy water and the wine. With a very non-Christian gesture, the Parish Priest gave him a push which made him fall to the ground. Not caring that they were in a church, Verdi retaliated with a strong **swear-word**, saying to the priest 'may heaven strike you!' The incident would probably have been forgotten, if an amazing thing had not happened a few years later, when the priest became the victim of a terrible accident, killed by a thunderbolt while he was officiating at Evening Prayer.

Roncole di Busseto, since renamed Roncole Verdi

The composer for freedom

From the first act of *Nabucco* which opened in 1842, it was clear that Giuseppe Verdi would become the voice of those who fought for the liberation of Italy from its foreign rule. The chorus of *Va pensiero*, heart of Verdi's drama, became a passionate hymn for the reclaiming of 'the country so beautiful and lost'. By the middle of the 1800s the phrase 'long live Verdi' was shouted or written. In Italian, this is written 'Vive Verdi' – which was the equivalent of writing **VIVA Victor Emmanuel Re (king) D'Italia**, or 'long live freedom'.

Scene from *Nabucco* by Verdi

*The soprano **Giuseppina Strepponi**, second wife of Giuseppe Verdi. She was a famous singer, who was forced to abandon the stage after having taken the part of Abigaille in **Nabucco** (1948), because the role weakened her voice.*

The composer who brought the German saga of the Nibelung to the stage

RICHARD WAGNER
(Leipzig 1813 – Venice 1883)

Wagner hurried along the crowded Bayreuth street, hardly able to contain his excitement. The time had come to tell his friends the great news – that work had finally finished on his Bayreuth Festival Theatre. Three long years had passed since he had helped in the laying of the first stone. Three endless years of sacrifice, appeals, difficulties, refusals, hopes … But now the Bayreuth Festival Theatre, the theatre built to stage his operas, was finished. All was now ready for the production of The Ring of the Nibelung, *the work where the last part depicted the twilight of the gods.*

For Richard Wagner, the summer of 1875 was a new beginning. From his **Bayreuth Festival Theatre** which had just been finished, the fame of the German composer would soon spread all over Europe. In the past, his compositions had been the object of fierce criticism and much reservation. But with the first performance of *The Ring of the Nibelung* in August 1876, he received recognition at last.

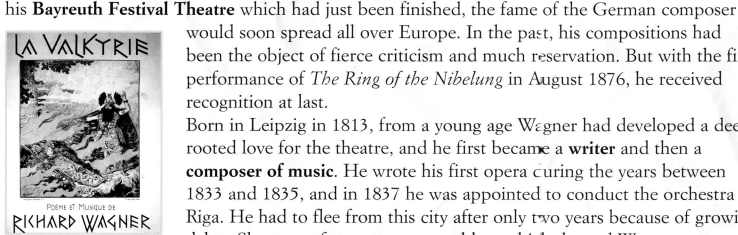

Born in Leipzig in 1813, from a young age Wagner had developed a deep-rooted love for the theatre, and he first became a **writer** and then a **composer of music**. He wrote his first opera during the years between 1833 and 1835, and in 1837 he was appointed to conduct the orchestra at Riga. He had to flee from this city after only two years because of growing debts. Shortage of money was a problem which dogged Wagner throughout his life, and the reason why he had to move from place to place so often, dodging the law and the people to whom he owed money. Meeting **King Ludwig II of Bavaria** in 1864 was a stroke of luck for Wagner. His Majesty became Wagner's great admirer and supporter. It was largely thanks to money from the king that Wagner succeeded in realizing his dream – a theatre to be built specifically to stage his operas.

Wagner died in Venice in 1883 and was buried at Bayreuth, the city where his Festival Theatre made him so famous.

Above, left: poster for Wagner's opera *The Valkyrie*; below, right: Wagner with his wife, Cosima, and the composer Franz Listz

Parsifal in a painting by Wiegand

A royal patron

Richard Wagner and **Ludwig II, King of Bavaria** met for the last time on 12 November 1880, when the composer conducted especially for the sovereign a preview of *Parsifal*, the opera which would be performed at Bayreuth in 1882. From that moment, their lives, which had been linked for the first time in 1864, would be separate. Whilst the composer continued his struggle with the arts and for the arts, the **patron king**, who had kept and supported the composer for over fifteen years, slipped into mental decline and then insanity (madness). On 13 June 1886, three years after the death of Wagner, Ludwig II, by then incapable of ruling his country and stripped of his title of king, ended his life by throwing himself into the waters of the lake at Starnberg.

A ghostly ship

Wagner's opera *The Flying Dutchman* tells the story of a Dutch captain who was so determined to sail around the Cape of Good Hope against the winds that he vowed he would do it even if it took him all eternity. From then on, evil spirits took command of his ship as part of a curse which condemned him to sail the seas until the end of time. The opera was inspired by the book *Memoirs of Herr Schnabelewopski* by the German writer **Heinrich Heine**. It came to Wagner's mind following an accident which happened in 1839. In that year, he had left Riga (in what is now Latvia) to flee debtors, intending to go to London. After many delays and accidents on the roads, he arrived at Pillau in north west Russia, where he boarded a ship. A few days after sailing, there was almost a shipwreck because of a violent **cloudburst**. From this frightening experience, Wagner knew exactly how it felt to be like a tiny little pawn in the hands of destiny, just like the main character in *The Flying Dutchman*.

Scene from *The Flying Dutchman* by Wagner

German roots

Wagner's masterpiece *The Ring of the Nibelung* is a complex work which comprises four separate operas – *Rhinegold*, *The Valkyries*, *Siegfried* and *The Twilight of the Gods*. It took the composer almost twenty three years to complete this tetralogy (a composition in four parts), from 1853, when he began writing *Rhinegold*, to 1876, the year when the entire ring cycle was staged for the first time at the Bayreuth Festival Theatre. The inspiration for the composition of this saga, centering on the dramatic meeting between men and God, came from the **Nibelungenleid** (singers of the Nibelung) a legendary tale in the German tradition written during the Middle Ages (fourteenth century).

Scene from *The Valkyries*

The jazz trombonist who brought music to the troops

GLENN MILLER

(Clarinda, Iowa 1904 – English Channel 1944)

The composer and jazz musician, Glenn Miller

Glenn Miller was the best-known American bandleader of the Second World War. After a career as a **professional trombonist** and then as a music arranger, he formed his own band in 1938 with a such a distinctive style that it was instantly recognized as 'the Glenn Miller sound', thanks to Miller's orchestrations of his own compositions, such as *Moonlight Serenade, String of Pearls* and *In the Mood*. The catchy rhythms and melodies of his music were particularly popular with the American and British troops, and this was the reason that Glenn Miller was flying to Paris on 16 December 1944, to play some of his music to help them celebrate Christmas and the liberation of Paris. By then he was a Major in the US Air Force, and so his take-off in a C-64 helicopter over the English Channel is well-recorded. What happened afterwards is a complete mystery. The helicopter failed to arrive in Paris. The most popular theory is that his helicopter was hit by **bomber aircraft**. But there was no report of any crash, and no bodies or wreckage of the helicopter were ever found. It seemed that Glenn Miller just disappeared. His desire to entertain the troops cost him his life. He had said that he wanted only to put 'a little joy into their hearts and a spring in their steps'.

Falling star

Ritchie Valens was an outstanding young Latin American musician, who became famous for re-writing *La Bamba*, a Mexican folk song, into the rock 'n' roll style of the 1950s. In 1959, his life was to end in a similar way to that of Glenn Miller's. On the evening of 2 February the seventeen year old singer, discovered only one year before by a record producer, left on a small tourist aeroplane. Shortly after take-off, there was a terrible crash on the runway, ending the life of the young man who had been looking forward to a wonderful musical career. The few songs which he composed, such as *Come On, Let's Go* and *Donna* became all-time hits within a short time. The 3 February, the day on which the remains of the aircraft were recovered, was called 'the day the music died' in the song *American Pie* by **Don McClean**, recently revived by the pop star Madonna.

TWO MUSICIANS AT THE CINEMA:
Both musicians died tragically in aircraft incidents and were subjects of films:
Glenn Miller *in 1953, on the life of the jazz composer, and the 1987 film*
La Bamba*, about Ritchie Valens (shown right in a performance).*

Index